To Ken & Nancy

with very best wishes

David

October 1994

# The Choice of the Private Trader

# The Choice of the Private Trader

The Private Market in Chinese Export Porcelain
illustrated from the Hodroff Collection

David S. Howard

Zwemmer

To the supercargoes and captains of the East India
Companies, without whose labours there would
have been no porcelain shipped from China for
the Private Trade.

© The Minneapolis Institute of Art 1994

First published 1994 by Zwemmer,
an imprint of Philip Wilson Publishers Ltd,
26 Litchfield Street, London WC2H 9NJ

ISBN 0 302 00642 7
LC 94-067101

Designed by Harold Bartram
Typeset by Southern Positives and Negatives (SPAN),
Lingfield, Surrey
Colour origination by Reprocolor International s.r.l.,
Milan, Italy
Printed and bound in Italy by Grafiche Milani

# Contents

# Preface

by the Director of the Minneapolis Institute of Arts

Porcelains have always been of great interest to American collectors of the decorative arts and no field of porcelain is more widely collected in the United States than wares produced by the Chinese for export. Given the strong commitment in this country, we have been enthusiastic about supporting David Howard's significant contribution to the study of Chinese Export porcelains by joining with Philip Wilson in the publication of this book. Combining new archival information with his many years of experience in the field, David Howard clarifies the role of the Private Trader in creating and disseminating the taste for the most aesthetically appealing of Chinese ceramic ware made for the European market. This volume also catalogues one of the most distinguished private collections of Chinese Export porcelains in the world: that formed by Leo and Doris Hodroff. The Institute's Decorative Arts and Sculpture Department together with Michael Conforti, the Institute's chief curator, who has overseen this project, have organized an exhibition of the Hodroff Collection that will travel to a number of other museums in North America.

I want to pay my deepest respect and express my sincere thanks to Leo Hodroff for his kindness and support during this entire project. Mr Hodroff began collecting Chinese Export porcelains more than four decades ago and as the years have progressed he has shown an increasing commitment to the addition of pieces of extraordinary rarity and quality whenever they become available. Leo Hodroff's foresight and dedication to collecting are true marks of the seriousness he devotes to his subject. The results are a cultural resource of significant consequence. We are honored to have the opportunity of sharing this outstanding collection with the public.

Evan Maurer
Director of the Minneapolis Institute of Arts

# Foreword

by The Earl of Perth, PC

When David Howard asked me to write a foreword to this book, there were three reasons why I couldn't refuse. The first was a friendship over forty years; the second was an opportunity to be involved in a book which I felt sure would add to the knowledge of all those who enjoy collecting Export porcelain; and the third reason was that my own ancestor, James Drummond, was one of those Private Traders of whom he writes. From 1801 to 1807 he was President of the Select Committee of the East India Company in Canton and his fine house and garden in Macao are today the City Museum. I am fortunate enough to have inherited some of the armorial porcelain, pictures and other objects that James Drummond, later restored to his Strathallan titles as 8th Viscount, brought home.

As a child I accepted without questioning that there were in our house many Chinese things including a lot of 'Lowestoft' – such was my ignorance of Chinese armorial and other porcelain. Over eighty years I have seen much and learnt much, making several visits to China, including a pilgrimage to Jingdezhen. It was during the time of Chairman Mao and we saw the factories still at work, but were much disappointed when our attempts at once again ordering some armorial porcelain failed. The Communist regime would have no truck with such privileged, degenerate and capitalist work! Now things are different – for in the end the Trader wins.

There is still much to learn, as this book shows, with its excellent illustrations from the outstanding Hodroff Collection. The subject is almost inexhaustible as all the great Western maritime powers, as well as the United States, commissioned porcelain from China, although the chapters which form the first part of this book relate how small a part of the whole China trade it was.

Despite the monopolies enjoyed by companies such as the East India Company, they could not compete in the end with the individual Private Trader. The extent of Chinese exports in Western style furniture, silver and pictures is still not fully appreciated, but porcelain has commanded greater attention and this book adds further to our knowledge and enjoyment of it.

Perth
October 1993

# Acknowledgements

This book is not the first to appear on the general subject of Chinese Export porcelain, and it will certainly not be the last. The subject has many avenues to explore and one by one they are being examined by those who are fascinated by this hybrid ware – as many have been since it first appeared in Europe nearly four hundred years ago.

I have drawn on many sources, both in writing chapters 1–4 and in the detailed study of the porcelain which follows. The principal sources for the preliminary chapters are referred to below and references are given to other works in the text that accompanies the illustrations which form the main part of this book; I have limited these in many cases to one example, reference to which will suffice to provide further comparisons.

Central to my own understanding of the East India Company, its servants and trade, has been *The Chronicles of the East India Company trading to China, 1635–1834* by Hosea Ballou Morse (1925). In his preface he tells of gaps and missing years in the records relating to China at the India Office Library in London, which is the fount of all information concerning the English trading in the East. Some of these gaps have since been filled by diligent research, but others still remain and may never be filled.

Morse, I think, would have been excited by some of the records on which he did not focus but which have since been published in the more specialized field of Chinese porcelain made for Europe. In this field Geoffrey Godden has listed a number of interesting records of orders, auctions and correspondence; François Hervouët, amongst others, had some success in identifying porcelain with the engravings it copied; and other authors have analysed records of sailings, captains and supercargoes and have had limited success in matching porcelain with descriptions in orders and invoices. In Holland, Christiaan Jörg has examined many records of the Dutch East India Company, while his work on Cornelis Pronk has given deep insight into the workings of the Dutch East India Company for that limited period. A number of discoveries of wrecks of the seventeenth and eighteenth centuries have, in recent years, focused attention on ships' manifests destined for Gothenburg and Amsterdam and remains of their cargoes that have been found. Study of the porcelain in particular has thrown a great deal of new light on the cargoes carried at specific dates, notably 1643, 1695 and 1752; and this book has benefited much from the knowledge gained by these finds.

I have been doubly fortunate in having not only these to refer to, but also the help of friends who have been very generous in sharing their knowledge with me – in particular Richard Kilburn who has spent a great deal of time studying East India records and has shared the discovery of documents such as instructions from the Court of Directors of the Hon. East India Company, and a considerable number of records of supercargoes and auctions together with lists of those who purchased at them.

Among these were records of chinaware and also shipments by supercargoes unearthed by Anthony Farrington, the Deputy Director of the British Library at the Oriental and India Office Collections, which I have studied and used, and I am grateful to him for this help. All these unedited manuscript notes (covering many facets of the trade as well as the porcelain) I have been able to use, thus providing a wealth of new material – particularly for parts of the chapters on Canton and the auctions. I have deliberately avoided using their references as footnotes and have abbreviated much of the material (without, I trust, destroying the balance), for I hope that one day a much more comprehensive study of these records may be published.

In a different field, the recent book by Bill Sargent, of the Peabody and Essex Museum of Salem, on the exciting collection of Chinese birds and animals formed by Pamela Copeland has provided a new yardstick by which the dating of these fascinating creations can be made. I would like to thank him for the discussions we have had about the examples in this book.

It has been reassuring and a great pleasure that John Ayers has read this manuscript and made a number of useful suggestions, for as one wades deeper and deeper into the vast volume of information available, it is sometimes difficult to see those details that prove a point among so many that just add to the story.

The book has been made possible by Leo and Doris

Hodroff and the Minneapolis Institute of Arts. Too often the role of the collector is overlooked, but without him many museums would never have opened and many subjects would still remain obscure. The true collector buys for pleasure, not profit, and his own tastes and knowledge are reflected in the choice he makes; his task requires patience and persistence and when successful his labours can be seen as a feat of craftsmanship itself – that must surely be so in this case. But the greatest pleasure for many collectors is to share the fruits of their years of painstaking acquisition with others, so that they may thereby learn better to enjoy the subject. That is undoubtedly the purpose of this book.

The taste of Leo and Doris Hodroff in choosing the pieces in their collection from the auction houses and antique shops of the Western world closely mirrors the tastes of the East India supercargoes who two centuries earlier faced a similar choice in the shops of Canton. With few exceptions – perhaps where unusual historical circumstances have been involved, for instance a salvaged cargo – the Hodroffs have been drawn to this finer ware and their collection is ideally suited to illustrating this book.

I am grateful to a number of other people without whose help it would have been difficult to write this book. To Evan Maurer, the Director of the Minneapolis Institute of Arts, who almost five years ago discussed the possibility of writing it and has displayed the nerve to see it through; to Michael Conforti, Chief Curator and Bell Curator of Decorative Arts and Sculpture at the Institute, who had the foresight to dream up the project in the first place and has smoothed its problems on both sides of the Atlantic; to Peter MacDonald and Stanley Eost for providing all the photographs in two whirlwind weeks in Minneapolis; and to the patience of everyone at Philip Wilson – some of whom I have got to know, and others who have been friends for more than sixteen years, I am most grateful. None of this assistance, however, would have sufficed had it not been for the help and patience of Leo and Doris Hodroff and for the constant encouragement and help of my wife, Angela, without whose work on the word processor and whose invaluable suggestions and improvements this book might never have been completed.


D.S.H.
West Yatton, 1993

# Introduction

... if you had been led to believe ... that the Private Trade china-ware is in general inferior to that of the Company's you have shewn yourselves possessed but of little knowledge, as the fact is notoriously the reverse ... we have an opportunity of knowing this by actual comparisons as both sorts go through the same channel of our sales and even the selling prices would prove the fact, if we had no other way of judging.

All the evidence today shows this letter, sent from London to the supercargoes in Canton in May 1790, to have been a masterly understatement. Indeed it was written in the year preceding the decision by the Court of the Hon. East India Company, perhaps the most powerful trading company the world has known, to withdraw from trading in porcelain on its own account after more than a century and a half during which tens of millions of pieces of chinaware had sailed in its ships to England – while the other maritime countries of Europe had achieved little less.

But who were the 'Private Traders', whose names today are little known and who had no company or fleet to compete with the vast resources of the East India Companies? And how could they possibly have succeeded in the way this letter appears to reveal? The chapters which form the first part of this book address these questions.

In particular, 'Captains and Supercargoes' tells how the East India Company attracted men of high calibre and skill but paid them no more than an average wage for their arduous and often hazardous journeys. This was achieved by allowing their officers to trade on their own account, on a scale which gradually increased as the eighteenth century wore on, while at the same time carrying out the Company's orders. Although the Company feared, with good reason, that the energies of its servants could be directed towards private gain at some expense to the profits of the shareholders, a careful use of Company duties and auction commissions ensured that the more successful an officer was, the more the Company benefited from these levies. All this happened within the closely knit circle of City and East India merchants who were often related to those same captains and supercargoes, so that the edifice survived – with great profit to all – for more than two centuries.

These chapters cannot, of course, encompass the whole picture of late seventeenth- and eighteenth-century trading between China and the West – even in porcelain. Indeed the author has neither the space nor the knowledge of languages to study the intricate workings of the East India Companies of France and Holland, Sweden and Denmark, and the records of Spain and Portugal – but there is little doubt that the problems encountered and solutions that evolved in England had similar parallels elsewhere. By the early part of the nineteenth century little remained of Company controls over the importation of Chinese porcelain. Meanwhile, from what they had seen from China, factories all over Europe had learned sufficient skills to meet the needs of the Western markets themselves.

One must remember that the entire Company trade in porcelain was probably little more than five per cent, and certainly less than ten per cent, of the trade with China in the eighteenth century. Although it varied from year to year, it is doubtful if the Private Trade in porcelain was as much as a quarter of the Company trade in that ware: yet in spite of its numerical insignificance, because it was based on the requirements of the most fashionable markets of the time, its artistic and historical importance is out of all proportion to its numbers. (In this respect there was a considerable difference from the Dutch trade where a more adventurous policy was pursued by the Company which itself bought a wide range of special designs.)

This market factor has had a distorting effect on our understanding of what we see today. For while the great majority of the millions of pieces ordered by the Company and used in homes across Britain have suffered irreparably and only a very small percentage remain, the Private Trade ware was in many cases used much more carefully (or not at all), and by the nineteenth century was either displayed in cabinets or stored in pantries, so that a very much larger part still survives.

It is not possible to identify with certainty today all the pieces of Chinese porcelain that were bought as part of the Private Trade, but in this book the great majority of those illustrated (except where specifically mentioned otherwise) were specially commissioned or bought for private speculative purchase. Certainly all armorial ware was privately ordered, and all political, religious, erotic, and numerous other groups copied after engravings. (It would have been risky, if not improper, for the Company to specify, for instance, such partisan subjects as Jacobite punch bowls.) It is also clear that most of the fine Yongzheng tea services and 'eggshell' porcelain plates would have been small speculative private purchases by officers or supercargoes in the Canton china shops.

As mentioned in chapter 3, the year 1774, for example, saw only two specified design patterns ordered by the Hon. East India Company for over a hundred thousand pieces of enamelled ware, and four specified designs among an even larger quantity of blue and white. In the same year, apart from the armorial services – which averaged at that time about fifty annually – there were probably hundreds of other individual pieces or designs chosen from Canton shops by servants of the East India Company. This may be an extreme example (although 1775 orders showed the same trend) but there is little doubt that although earlier in the century many charming, and today rare, designs were bought for the Company, as the century wore on, the Company took fewer risks and the Private Trade chose more widely for itself.

This book is, in fact, a tale of porcelain that sees the trade in oriental chinaware for Europe through the eyes of those who bought and sold it. Their choice was directed towards securing the most attractive porcelain at a price that would sell well both at auction and privately, while also fuelling the craze for things Chinese. Anyone aware of the workings of the City of London today will recognize the pragmatism and conflicts of interest, the self-regulatory organization of the East India Company and the successes and excesses of those who traded under its aegis for almost two centuries.

The Hon. East India Company itself had little interest in Chinese porcelain except as a successful product for marketing in Europe. Its evident lack of

East India House; engraving, 1851

enthusiasm echoes from an early dispatch which reports that Canton was 'destitute of all sorts of commodities . . . either silks raw or wrought, or China-root . . . nor indeed anything but Chinaware . . . .' Its servants, however, sought to promote a product of fashion which, if well handled, could excite their wealthy friends, relatives and clients – and at considerable profit, for it was not available elsewhere. But first they had to choose well and often risk their own capital on that choice. A number were beguiled by the porcelain and bought it for themselves. That it was well chosen is evident, and although the untold numbers of Chinese potters and painters remain anonymous, its quality and delicacy is a tribute to the generations of skill that lay behind their craftsmanship.

The main part of this book is devoted to illustrations of this privately ordered ware, although a number of pieces that were part of Company cargo are also included. All are from the collection of Leo and Doris Hodroff of Minneapolis, which is perhaps today the largest and most comprehensive of its kind in private hands.

The arrangement of the porcelain breaks new ground in a number of respects. Some books have their illustrations arranged by subject-matter or border design; they analyse the styles of painting, and the markets for which they were intended. Yet others have pieces selected because of the story they have to tell. This book presents a different arrangement, aiming to treat the material in a way close to that of the market itself; in this way it is hoped that developments in the trade may be more fully understood.

The porcelain is thus divided into six broad groups according to use, which are as clear today as at the time the porcelain was made. They are: dinner services, tea and coffee sets, drinking vessels, other personal and everyday utensils, decorative vases, and finally, human and animal figures. These groups need little introduction; they are themselves subdivided so that each subgroup – plates and dishes, tureens, teapots, cups and saucers and so on – is treated in its own chronological order; in fact we see the pieces, regardless of their decoration or subject-matter, in the way that they were first seen by the captains and supercargoes who commissioned them in Canton, or perhaps chose them from the shelf in a china shop in 'Thirteen Factory Street' behind the European hongs on the Pearl River.

While plates varied in overall size, breadth of rim and sometimes border shape or moulding, they were similar and, in general, essentially round. Tureens or teapots, however, reflected the silver or porcelain models supplied in a range of national variations and this makes such pieces particularly interesting, sometimes indicating the market concerned. Animals and birds stemmed from both Chinese and European origins; and early Chinese parrots were later joined by copies of Kaendler's figures from Meissen.

There is still some way to go, however, before the picture is fully clear. For example, one would like to know exactly when the buying of teapots, tea cups and other tea equipage separately in bulk by the Companies became the buying of 'tea setts'; clearly the Private Trade at least was doing this by 1720 with its armorial ware. One would also like to know when the first soup tureen became part of a standard service and when dinner services were ordered as large units. Evidence from the Dutch East India ship *Geldermalsen* which sank in 1752 shows that the V.O.C. was then importing all the elements of dinner services, but leaving them to be assembled in any way the china shops in Europe chose. We do know, however, that tureens were part of armorial services bought by the Private Trade twenty years earlier.

In England a comparatively small circle of related families, related by blood or background, succeeded both in directing what became the largest company in the world and at the same time in acquiring much of the porcelain that survives today – examples of which are illustrated in this book. But while these families also commissioned their own armorial services, so often the only porcelain it is still possible to identify in records, the rest was ordered in Canton by supercargoes and captains. They sailed with the Company and were its servants, but followed their own taste and employed their personal allowances in exercising their choice as Private Traders.

# 1 The East India Trade and its Porcelain

Viewed from seventeenth-century Europe, the extraordinary growth of the newly discovered world could well be seen as entering a stage of adjustment and consolidation after the startling discoveries of the sixteenth century. Only three decades had elapsed between Columbus discovering America and Magellan's ship completing its voyage of circumnavigation in 1522 – a feat generally ascribed to Magellan although in fact completed without him. As that century wore on, the world took shape until it had, with the exception of Australasia, come almost fully into western view.

Long before the sixteenth century was at an end, the maritime states of Europe had turned their attention from discovery to commerce and conquest, even if at first on a scale so modest as to have left most of the newly discovered lands unaware of their true aims: of their search for gold, and the spread of their influence and religion.

In 1519 the Portuguese had reached Canton but had been refused permission to trade there by the Ming Emperor of China – ruler of by far the most powerful country in the East – and only in 1557 were they allowed to settle on the peninsula of Macao at the mouth of the Pearl River. The Jesuit missionary Francis Xavier had died five years earlier on an island close to Canton, but while the efforts of the church to gain a permanent and effective base in China were never really successful, trade, on the other hand, was to lead three centuries later to war and to the humbling of the Ching dynasty and its eventual fall in the early twentieth century.

Such an outcome was hardly to be foreseen when, in the 1570s with Papal approval, Spain and Portugal agreed to divide the world's trade routes between them – all to the East to Portugal and all to the West to Spain – so that Spanish galleons sailed from Manila to Central America, transporting their cargoes by land for the final voyage from the Caribbean to Cadiz, while from the Portuguese colonies at Macao and Goa a steady stream of luxuries travelled via the Cape to the port of Lisbon.

The exploits of adventurers such as Francis Drake, who in 1579 captured a heavily laden Spanish galleon with a vast cargo in the Pacific (including porcelain,

some pieces of which he gave to Queen Elizabeth), were followed by a decade made notable by the defeat of the Spanish Armada in the Channel. These successes encouraged both the English and the Dutch to enter this rapidly growing and lucrative trade themselves which, after some exploratory ventures, they did in the opening years of the seventeenth century. A monopoly company – 'The Governor and Merchants of London trading into the East Indies' – was established in England in 1600, and in 1602 the Verenigde Oost Indische Compagnie (V.O.C.), the Dutch East India Company, was founded in Holland. Unlike the Spanish and Portuguese, these companies planned to develop trade on a truly European scale.

It was the Dutch who displayed the greater effort throughout much of the seventeenth century, creating trade links with China and also with Japan which, with the exception of China itself, were to become exclusive. These were largely from their main trading centre in the Pacific at Batavia (now Jakarta), matching the way in which the Spanish had already developed their own base at Manila. For a period the city of Batavia traded freely and mainly on its own account with China and, throughout that century and the next, a steady flow of Chinese vessels brought goods of all kinds to Java at prices little higher than those in Canton, but with a substantial saving in cost of shipping and time. Although the English developed the port of Bantam on the coast to the west of Batavia, it never played the pivotal role that Batavia did in the Dutch trade. The Portuguese, meanwhile, were content to rely on their foothold at Macao, which acted under the nominal control of their Governor-General at Goa in India.

The English were not as successful as the Dutch in establishing trading relations and for some years made efforts to trade jointly with the Portuguese, this being much to the advantage of the latter. King Charles I, who had confirmed the monopoly to the London Company, nevertheless invested personally in the stock of a rival company founded by Sir William Courteen in 1635. In spite of difficulties and delays, four of its ships reached Goa and Canton in 1637 and, after threats and further delays from both the Chinese and Portuguese, managed to trade in sugar, ginger, cloves and even fifty-three tubs of chinaware, but at no profit to the shareholders after a round voyage of over 36,000 miles.

The period of the Civil War in England from 1640 and the Commonwealth which followed saw only one London ship at Macao, when the *Hinde* tried to trade there in 1644 – the last year of the Ming Dynasty – but found it '. . . destitute of all sorts of commodities; there not being to be bought in the City either silks raw or wrought, or Chinaroot . . . nor indeed anything but Chinaware, which is the bulk of the Hinde's lading, the rest being bought in gold' (report from Surat of 1654).

Although two private English vessels, the *King Ferdinand* and the *Richard and Martha*, were at Canton in 1658, they left without a cargo because of the high dues levied by the Chinese customs. The next venture of the London Company was in 1664, soon after the Restoration of the Monarchy – but this again was scarcely profitable, and it was not until the 1670s that the scale of trading profits became such as to attract wider attention in England. In 1686 the Court of the London Company was able to report that 'as the Chyna Trade is becoming more promising, Teas and Spices are, in future, to form Part of the Company's Imports and not to be articles of Private Trade'.

A period of peace and relative prosperity in England during the reign of Charles II rebuilt the fortunes of many landed and aristocratic families and the late seventeenth century saw a growing mobility between these and the wealthy merchant dynasties in London, who, having already benefited greatly from trading in Turkey and the Levant, were now poised to take advantage of opportunites in the wider world. This required ocean-going vessels for trade as opposed to those that had in the past mainly navigated the waters of the Channel and the North Sea – thus leading in turn to an increasingly prosperous ship-building community at Blackwall and Deptford on the River Thames.

Until 1639, ships were built at the expense of the trading companies, but it was then decided that it would be more economical to charter vessels – something that came at an opportune moment for the London Company with the downturn in trade that attended the Civil War. With a few earlier exceptions, the usual size was 500 tons, although occasionally this was officially recorded as the size when the ship was actually larger.

With growing private ownership of vessels from 1660 onwards, it was inevitable that the merchants in any ship-owning syndicate, who provided the capital for the vessel and frequently the private cargo, should have considerable influence in the appointment of captains, who in turn were responsible for selecting the crew. Thus, until the end of the eighteenth century, if a captain retired or died, it was likely that he would be succeeded by a relative – as happened when the *Shaftesbury*, commanded by Captain Matthew Bookey, arrived in Canton in 1746, but owing to his illness, returned under Captain William Bookey.

The system of ship-owning syndicates developed in such a way that by the beginning of the eighteenth century some merchants were acting in a number of capacities – chartering their own ships, owning private cargoes and also holding seats on the Court of Directors of the East India Company. This was not at first considered to pose any conflict of interest, even when the merchants negotiated the charter rates with the Company, but it was not long before it was seen by shareholders as prejudicial to their dividends if excessive rates were paid for ships which drained the profits on the cargoes carried. Although a series of regulations led to a more open system of tendering and directors of the Company were officially barred from having shares in a ship, the fact that the English East India Company did not build their own ships throughout the eighteenth century speaks for the closely knit relationship that prevailed between the merchants, ship-owners and Company directors – and this was an occasional focus of discontent.

It was unusual for merchants to own whole vessels, but having agreed a share, they would commission one of the major ship-builders to build a ship. Once this was arranged, they would negotiate a rate per ton with the Company. This agreed rate also led to the pay of ships' officers being in part a free allowance for cargo.

Perhaps the principal ship-builder was Sir Henry Johnson of Blackwall and Aldborough who in 1692 married as his second wife Anne, later Baroness Wentworth in her own right. It was he who owned the first armorial Chinese porcelain with English arms. But this was only symptomatic of the social changes afoot after the Protestant William of Orange came to the throne of England in 1689 to rule jointly with Mary, the daughter of the Catholic James II. Throughout the eighteenth century the great wealth of merchants increasingly found its way into the older landed and aristocratic families, and an analysis of the directors, governors, captains, managing owners and supercargoes of this period shows that more than 60 per cent were from armigerous families (those granted coats of arms) – then the yardstick of the English or Scottish gentleman. (This is clear from the fact that 60 per cent had armorial dinner and tea services made for them in China and the full figure must therefore be even higher). Of the whole population of Britain less than 2 per cent were entitled to arms.

In 1698, opposition to the structure and management of the London Company had grown to such a degree that King William chartered a new company, 'The English Company Trading to the East Indies', and this resulted in a greater number of English ships trading at Canton. In 1708 the two English companies merged to become known formally as 'The Honourable East India Company'. It was to become perhaps the largest company the world has known, with assets which at one time boasted most of the subcontinent of India and a large standing army there, islands such as St Helena (leased to the British Government at the time of Napoleon's last exile), and enormous influence stretching from South-East Asia to Europe. For much of the eighteenth century it paid dividends to its shareholders of up to 12 per cent at a time when this was far in excess of normal returns, and as a result its stock traded at well above its issued price.

All this had grown within a century from painstaking but uninspiring beginnings and great financial risks, but the profits to be made in trading with India and China outshone any that might have been made before the industrial revolution by trading within Europe; for when a ship came home safely, the products that it brought were probably not available from other sources and, as luxuries, could support a generous price structure with little competition. From the second half of the seventeenth century the most important cargoes were tea and gold, but increasingly porcelain was seen as a useful and decorative cargo – for the new drink of tea tasted at its best from chinaware, while the garnitures were particularly decorative on great fireplaces such as those at Hampton Court and Burghley and other great houses in England, while on the Continent, Augustus King of Saxony collected it for his mirrored halls and as inspiration for the porcelain factory he supported at Meissen.

In 1700 it would have been impossible to conceive of the volume of specially commissioned porcelain ware that would be made in China during the coming hundred years. Of the English armorial services (which are almost the only pieces that can be identified from contemporary records with certainty today) perhaps only three had been made by 1705 – those for Sir Henry Johnson, for Governor Pitt of Fort St George (the founder of the greatest political family of the century) and for Sir William Juxon, a relatively obscure country gentleman from Gloucestershire

whose uncle, Bishop Juxon, had attended Charles I on the scaffold. Most of the small number of early armorial services which followed were ordered for East India governors, captains and merchants – indeed there are few armorial services before 1720 with English arms which are not linked to the Hon. Company. A century later, perhaps as many as five thousand British families owned such services.

By 1730 the fashion for Chinese silks, wallpapers, lacquer and particularly porcelain had spread to a great number of the richer country families. Admiral Viscount Torrington, First Lord of the Admiralty, 1727–33, had a particularly magnificent service – the only other one of similar design being made for his friend, Admiral Thomas Mathews, who had commanded the English Fleet in the East Indies and later in the Mediterranean (where he was unsuccessful in blockading Toulon and, after a five-year trial, was dismissed for negligence in 1747).

Admiral Mathews was able to enjoy retirement in the knowledge that he was the victim of political intrigue, but Lord Torrington's son, Admiral George Byng, who built Wrotham Park in Hertfordshire and intended to decorate it with a fine collection of Chinese porcelain figures, was in 1755 accused of cowardice off Majorca and mercilessly lampooned by the English press, while broadsheets were published showing him giving orders to run from the French while his cabin shelves were loaded with Chinese porcelain figures. The fact that there were other broadsheets just as scurrilous but with a cabin scene omitting the Chinese figures suggests that the story was apocryphal – but Admiral Byng was shot on his own quarterdeck in 1757. (One of his finest figures is illustrated later in this book.) Could it be that Chinese porcelain, so long the epitome of everything fashionable, was now regarded by some as a distraction and against the national interest?

This incident certainly had little effect on the East India Company in a year during which the heavily outnumbered army of Colonel Clive was to triumph at Plassey, effectively conquering most of India for the Company. It may, however, have marked the pinnacle of the craze for Chinese porcelain, for 1757 also saw great steps forward in the enamel painting of porcelain at the Worcester factory, the first full year of William Duesbury at Derby and the new gold anchor mark at Chelsea. Henceforward Chinese porcelain was only one of the several fine ceramic wares available in England.

In other countries of Europe the trade with China developed in different ways, but along parallel lines, which took into account their domestic production –

Cartoon of the cabin of Admiral the Hon. George Byng,
1755 – above him a porcelain head and chinaware on the
shelves *Copyright British Museum*

principally Meissen porcelain in Germany, Sèvres
porcelain in France and delftware in Holland. The
French traded as a company at Canton from 1699 until
the ending of their charter in 1769, and the private
French ships that succeeded the Company ceased to sail
at the time of the Revolution. The Ostend Company,
under a charter from the Emperor of Austria, was
short-lived, ceasing to trade in 1727 when its Scottish
Director, Colin Campbell, who had fled England to
escape his creditors during the crisis of the 'South Sea
Bubble', went to Sweden and was far more successful
at Gothenburg. For almost a century this city was the
headquarters of the Swedish Company.

The Danish Altona Company thrived from about
1731 until the end of the century, while the
Brandenburg Company existed for a very short period
and the Prussian Asiatic Company ceased to trade in
1763 at the end of the Seven Years War. In most cases,
however, enterprising merchants carried on trading
privately and by the end of the century, when the
Hon. East India Company was still protecting its
position at Canton against private English traders, the
post of Prussian Consul was filled by an English
merchant, Daniel Beale, enabling him to trade with
some legitimacy outside the rules of the Hon.
Company (and to purchase one of the largest later
services of armorial porcelain in about 1800). His son,
Thomas, followed him in this post but was later
bankrupt after dealing in opium bonds.

While the number of English ships trading at

Canton continued to grow from 40 in the 1740s, and 70 in the 1750s, to between 180 and 190 in the 1770s and each of the next three decades, the volume of porcelain did not match this growth and the 1750s saw by far the greatest number of armorial services ordered – about twice as many as in any subsequent decade (this being the best yardstick too for all specially commissioned and Private Trade wares).

There was no sudden fall in armorial or other private orders, but the enormous popularity enjoyed by the finest porcelain in the first half of the century now encouraged a growing middle class to adopt the style in their turn – so often the death knell of any high fashion. Services and punch bowls for Societies and City Livery Companies were followed by wares decorated for inns and tradesmen, including occasionally a china shop, and by the 1780s anyone could order a service with personal initials and a pseudo crest of two birds to indicate marital bliss or an anchor to remind a sailor of his years at sea. By the turn of the nineteenth century it is doubtful if more than half a dozen armorial services were being made each year for the British market although the volume of initialled wares was still considerable.

The Americans had joined the China Trade on their own account in 1784 with the voyage of the *Empress of China* from New York to Canton; before that, however, a considerable volume of porcelain had been bought at auction in Europe by china wholesalers to be shipped to the flourishing cities of the East Coast. This commerce had its origin in the much earlier voyages of Dutch ships which were trading at New Amsterdam and at the first Williamsburg settlement as early as 1620. Trading by both English and Dutch ships at Boston, New York and up the Hudson River to Albany, and at Philadelphia, Baltimore, Washington, Williamsburg and Charleston had continued throughout the seventeenth and eighteenth centuries, with special orders being placed by American families as early as 1660; colonial houses in Boston, on the

Hudson River, New York and further south have records of such purchases made through merchants in London and Amsterdam.

It was this enforced reliance on the European market and the taxes that had to be paid, not only on porcelain but to a much greater degree on teas, silks and other wares, that was a major complaint leading to the War of 1775. After it was over, the major American ports prepared to trade with China directly – not through any great Company, but on their own account.

There was no American East India Company, but Elias Haskett Derby of Salem, Samuel Shaw of Boston, William Duer of New York, Robert Morris of Philadelphia and Captain Stewart Dean of Albany were men in the mould of the managing owners, captains and supercargoes of the East India Company – indeed, few European captains could rival the first sailing of Captain Dean who, in the fall of 1785, took the sloop *Experiment* of 80 tons to Canton and back with a crew of eleven, returning seventeen months later without any loss of men and 'thirteen sets of chinaware to order, for such families as could afford and thought proper to indulge in such luxuries'.

While the Hon. East India Company had ceased to import porcelain on its own account by 1795 and almost all orders for porcelain from any source placed in Canton after 1800 were for the Private Trade of supercargoes and captains or for private merchants, it was the Americans, who had no domestic manufacture of their own, who continued to order commissioned services with crests and initials into the 1880s.

As late as the 1860s, Captain Daniel Ammen brought back from China six enamelled services with initials including those of William Seward, Secretary of State, and Ulysses Grant, whose service of over 300 pieces was delivered to the White House shortly after his inauguration in 1869. They travelled with another service of 150 pieces with the initial A – for his own private use.

# 2 Captains and Supercargoes

It is clear that while many historical, social and fashion factors in the seventeenth to nineteenth centuries affected the import from China of objects that today would be considered 'decorative arts', it was the captains, officers and supercargoes who were responsible for obtaining and choosing these wares.

The trade in teas, spices, metals and even everyday porcelain was a largely commercial enterprise which usually, although not always, accounted for ninety per cent of the cargoes and was designed to supply the retail and manufacturing trades in Britain and elsewhere with the 'raw materials' they needed. The East India Companies were best suited to organize this. When it came to the individual tastes of wealthy clients, however, it was the captains, officers and supercargoes who could translate their wishes into realities, particularly as most understood these tastes, which were also their own; for more than half of them were related to the landed classes who, until later in the eighteenth century, were the main buyers of such luxuries.

It is important to remember that the pragmatic attitude of the Hon. East India Company caused frequent alterations in the remuneration of its servants; it was, however, their underlying policy to attract men of calibre and ability who would benefit the Company, whilst allowing the most able to prosper. Social background and connections may have played a major role in deciding whether a junior supercargo could rise to Chief of Council and so to the Court (board) of the Company, or merely enabled him to earn very substantially more than was then common. In the case of captains, we have already seen that family connections played an important part in their chance of having a command.

The Company can also be seen today as much more 'democratic' than most organizations of that period for while, early in the eighteenth century, the rules allowed captains to carry £300 of Private Trade, at the lower end of the scale even ordinary seamen were permitted to carry £10 – all with a commission to the Company of 5 per cent. While discipline was strict and life hard on Company vessels, there are numerous records of sailors trying to transfer from naval to East India Company ships and there is no question of any

organization similar to the infamous press gang being required to recruit crews for East Indiamen.

In the early eighteenth century the salary of a captain was £120 per year; the round voyage was three years including his shore leave in England, and he lived free for about two-thirds of that time. It is not clear exactly how much a captain could make on a voyage because he was able to charge for passengers, carry private orders from acquaintances and handle speculative buying, on which his profit on the outward voyage was rolled into his buying capital in Canton; his eventual profit could not be known until the auction results in London, often three years after the ship first sailed. A total of up to £10,000 for a three-year journey is probably not an exaggeration for a successful voyage.

Captains were allowed to charge on an agreed scale for passengers sailing to India or Canton – most were East India Company servants – but as many as ten passengers on some journeys each way would have given the captain between £2,000 and £3,000 in all, depending on whether they ate at the captain's table or with the junior officers.

Private Trade allowances were not confined to the homeward journeys, so that a captain with contacts in Bombay or Madras could carry luxuries to merchants there at considerable profit and free of any company freight charges, and also to China, where such diverse goods as watches, clocks, spectacles and firearms found ready buyers; mirrors were bought by workshops in Canton and later resold as reverse paintings on glass to European traders. He did not have to pay freight on the scale agreed by the Company for his own private purchases, but Company instructions make it very clear that all other cargoes had to have freight charged at the appropriate rate for that vessel.

The final gain accruing to the captain (or supercargo) depended on whether the capital deployed was his own or was advanced by family or commercial friends, or even whether he was working on commission for a London merchant. Such detailed records are now all lost – indeed, some may never have been committed to paper.

The scale on which a captain traded varied from the 1680s onwards. In 1683 he could carry £200 of permitted goods for every 100 tons weight of the ship, with other officers on a sliding scale of £60 to £10. This was increased to £300 in 1702.

There were occasions when captains carried more than the permitted scale and after a number of successful auctions when it was quite clear that this was happening, the Company in 1733 accepted the inevitable, applying an additional commission of 15 per cent on all auction results over £2,500. Later in the century it became increasingly common for captains to use some of their own private cargo as 'dunnage' – packaging as protection for the main cargo which filled spaces not normally allowed as cargo space. In spite of some Company complaints, the goods went to auction and as the Company profited, this practice was largely overlooked.

Perhaps the most comprehensive study of the role of the supercargo was undertaken by Morse in *The East India Company Trading to China* (1925); this work explores not only the role allotted to him by the East India Company, but his own financial involvement in the trade over much of the eighteenth century as a private trader. Morse quotes from Company records year by year from 1699 to 1754 when there is a gap until 1774, and after that date until 1834; although in this later period it is a much more general comparison of the trade between the countries trading at Canton.

The supercargo had to be a linguist and a diplomat, a merchant and banker, an individual and an employee of the Company at the same time, as well as being able, well educated, and incorruptible. He was responsible for the cargo with which each ship set sail for China and had to sell it for the best sum available in India or China itself. If he sold in India, or even Sumatra or Java, he would take on other goods for sale in China. When ships left their home port they carried not less than one tenth of the value of their cargo in English manufactured products, the rest probably being lead or silver. The value of the outward cargo was its capital and the supercargo's judgement on such matters as the exact amount paid in China for teas or silks, or whether the Company could make more profit in London by buying quicksilver or vermilion, was crucial. Since he held the money, he had to decide how much should be advanced to Chinese merchants to buy the cargoes on which they had agreed.

Yet the salaries of the supercargoes, as those of the ships' captains and officers, were very low. Morse quotes the salary of the chief of the 'factory' at Amoy in 1681 at £80 per year and those of his council at £40 each – how were men of ability to be attracted to such posts?

The solution to this impossible situation was to allow supercargoes to trade on their own account. The earliest figures available show that in 1674 the Company invested £430,000 in stock for 'the Indies' and their ships returned with goods valued at £860,000. At the same time they allowed the supercargoes, captains and officers to invest the very large sum of £135,000; their return is not recorded, but it would be surprising if it were less than the 100 per cent profit on the Company trade. Clearly such a policy was open to the risk of abuse even if only by the disproportionate effort that supercargoes would put into the different facets of their task.

Nor was it just a simple question of Private Trade and Company trade, for in their role as the Company's servants, supercargoes had reason to be suspicious of ships' officers both in their relationship with Chinese merchants and in their use of cargo space, particularly as their concessions, as we have seen, differed from those of the supercargoes. In 1715 the Directors questioned the fact that the captains and officers had imported 20,000 lbs of tea on their own account which had a detrimental effect on the Company trade, which that year was scarcely larger.

In the 1690s the Company agreed to Private Trade on the liberal condition that 20 per cent of the Private Trade profit 'shall be ours in consideration of our running the hazard of the sea, general charges of the Company, and disbursements aforesaid of our money in India'. The rest was to be kept by the supercargo – with the further qualification that in time of war the Company's share should be 40 per cent.

By 1700 the Company would lay down terms from time to time on which it would permit Private Trade by supercargoes on the ships it was chartering. On the *Eaton* in 1699 it allowed private trade of £3,500 of which £1,500 could be in goods of their choice and £2,000 in either gold from China or diamonds purchased on the Coromandel coast.

During the next fifteen years, the Company found it more advantageous to give supercargoes a commission on the Company trade at the same time as restricting their private trading. In the early eighteenth century this varied from $3\frac{1}{2}$ per cent to 4 per cent on the whole cargo with the senior supercargo taking about half and the other two dividing the remainder.

Competition between the supercargoes on different ships was also not to the advantage of the Company, and this led to a new system in 1715 which created a Council of all the supercargoes in that year from any British ship in Canton. Their commission was shared in an agreed way, and in 1722 this was formalized into three forms of remuneration: an 'allowance', a 'permission' and a 'privilege'. These were defined as:

'Allowance' of a portion of the Company's stock from which profits were to be given to the supercargoes in agreed proportion (effectively a commission).
'Permission' for each supercargo to carry out an agreed sum in silver and to bring back its equivalent in gold. (Gold was less highly prized in China in relation to silver than in Europe and thus a certain profit could be made).
'Privilege' of Private Trade in goods of his choice both ways.

In 1722 the seven supercargoes on the three ships arriving at Canton that year were Mr James Naish (chief), Mr Newnam, Mr Savage, Mr Pratt, Mr Turner, Mr Dubois and Mr Talbot, and their combined remuneration for the voyage was:

|  | Allowance | Permission | Privilege | Salary over 3 years |
|---|---|---|---|---|
|  | £11,000 | £5,400 | £900 | (not given) |
| of which the chief had: | £3,000 | £1,500 | £200 | £240 |

In addition, they were not subject to freight or other charges.

There are similar records for other years, but 1722 gives a fair idea of the arrangement and it must be borne in mind that all the elements attracted a profit margin; at this time, however, it was normally possible to sail to China only once in three years, and about fifteen months were spent at sea, six months at Canton and fifteen months 'at rest' in England. Improvements in sailing and trading enabled this to become a two-year cycle later in the century, and eventually an annual one.

When everything is taken into account, the figures show that in the 1720s chief supercargoes normally had remuneration of between £1,500 and £2,500 per year – £4,500 to £7,500 per journey (perhaps equivalent to the pay of chief executives of major companies today, although without their tax). This may have been exceeded on a successful voyage and when auction results were good in London.

To what extent the Private Trade consisted of porcelain is not usually clear, although as many as five of the supercargoes in 1722 are known to have ordered armorial dinner services for their families and probably obtained a number of others for acquaintances (these, however, almost certainly followed on a later ship).

By 1730 this system had settled into a regular pattern and it is possible to give specific examples which throw light on the question. The figures quoted by Morse are random and usually not exactly comparable year by

year, but probably give an accurate idea of trading.

That year the Company trade totalled approximately £198,500 (595,824 taels) on four ships. The largest amount of Private Trade was done by Captain Thomas Gilbert of the *Prince of Wales* who carried goods on his own account of £3,890 of which £2,500 was gold, £763 was tea and £595 was porcelain. All these figures represent his investments and the eventual profit is likely to have been between 50 per cent and 100 per cent or more depending on the skill of the officer and the type of goods carried.

In 1732, again with four vessels, the senior supercargoes had a similar scale set out to that of 1722, the four captains being allowed together to buy up to £4,000 of gold and to use 13 tons of space for their own cargoes.

The following year 'the officers' on the *Wyndham* under Captain Lyell are recorded as carrying £6,100 of Private Trade of which £2,755 was gold, £767 was tea, £960 was silks, £694 was lacquer, mother-of-pearl and other goods and £908 was chinaware (this may also have included Captain Lyell's armorial service).

In 1734 both Captain Hudson of the *Harrison* and Captain Martin of the *Grafton* had 13 tons each for their private cargo but no details are given of this, while the Company trade for the two vessels is given as £98,800 of which only £3,000 was porcelain. (The porcelain was packed in 240 chests which can be compared with the ships of other nations in Canton that year – the French, 154 chests plus 200 bundles; the Danish, 248 chests; and the Dutch, 163 chests.)

In 1735 the supercargoes on the three ships had similar concessions to those in earlier years and the only recorded private cargo is that of Captain Bootle of the *Houghton*, who carried for his own account value of £2,880 of which £901 was gold, £1,027 was tea and £372 was chinaware (it is possible that this included two armorial services made for the Bootle family, for there are a number of 'tubs' and 'chests' of porcelain recorded; however, his private cargo surprisingly also included '16,000 teacups, coarse [and] 7,400 plates coarse'). This compares with a total of 430,000 pieces of porcelain shipped by the Company on the three ships.

Details of private cargoes for the 1736 season are given for the two supercargoes on the *Richmond*, amounting to £5,252 – of which £4,404 was gold, £408 was 'cornelian beads' and only £204 was chinaware.

It would be possible to continue in this way but it would not be relevant to this book. It does, however, appear that very occasionally the Private Trade in porcelain could be greater than the Company's own, and in spite of efforts by the Company to remove the underlying conflict between the interests of the supercargoes, captains and officers, and those of the Company, this was not entirely successful; although in the end the Company profited in one way or another.

In terms of porcelain it is only possible to relate quantities and values approximately. The Company cargo of £3,000 worth of porcelain in 1734 may have cost an average of approximately $1\frac{1}{2}$d per piece in Canton, meaning that about 480,000 pieces were being carried. Calculations for Private Trade would be much less accurate but the evidence of earlier auction values suggests that much, if not all of the Private Trade (note Captain Bootle's cargo in 1735 above) was in more expensive wares costing perhaps ten times as much as Company or 'coarse' goods. This enables one to estimate that captains or supercargoes who brought back £500 worth of porcelain averaging 15d each would have had 7,500 pieces (approximately equal to nineteen standard *famille rose* dinner services of 400 pieces each or its equivalent).

In 1731 the 424 pieces of a fine armorial *famille rose* service for Sir Charles Peers which included 68 dishes, sauce boats, mugs, ewers etc. cost £76, or 43d each; while at the same time a well painted underglaze blue service of 255 pieces made for his son, and with the Peers crest only, cost £13 6s 8d, – or 12d each. This would seem to bear out the approximate calculation in the previous paragraph.

More than one captain or supercargo, on whose ability depended so much of the success of the Company's trade in the East, rose to become managing owner of a fleet of vessels, or chairman of the Hon. East India Company. Captain Robert Preston, who first commanded the *Asia* at Canton in 1768, was managing owner of twenty-five ships there between 1784 and 1800 – by which time he had also succeeded his brother to the family baronetcy and had inherited the three Preston armorial services.

John Roberts, who spent many years in China as a merchant and had a home in Macao, became Chairman of the Hon. East India Company in 1802. By this time he owned no fewer than five armorial services at his estate at Bonnington, and another decorated with Chinese figures and gilding; a design known today as 'palace ware'.

His contemporary and fellow director, Thomas Fitzhugh (whose father, William, had sailed to China in 1714 as captain of the *Derby*), was himself a supercargo at Canton on a number of occasions between 1746 and 1767. He was President of the Council for two seasons from 1779, and a Director of the Company from 1787 until his death in 1800. In this century his name has become associated with a number of related designs of chinaware and it is perhaps better known today than when he first chose a dinner service of that pattern in 1780.

# 3 Canton

When an East Indiaman reached the anchorage at Whampoa it was after a journey of five to seven months from Europe. If English, it may have called at Bombay or Madras, or even at Bantam in Java, to trade at those ports – selling some of its outward cargo, and taking on board further goods which might be wanted at Canton. But however important this trading might be, it was not as important as arriving in Canton early in the new season.

The 'season' was decreed by the monsoon winds which in the early summer allowed square-rigged vessels to run up the South China Seas on the South-West monsoon, whether from the Sunda Straits between Java and Sumatra or the Malacca Straits between Sumatra and Malaya. The South China Seas are beset with shoals and not only was it far quicker to run straight before the wind to the mouth of the Pearl River, but far safer than beating against the wind, with the danger of striking an uncharted reef.

If all went well, ships started arriving in Canton in late June or early July, but the South-West monsoon blew until October. On the return trip it was possible to leave on the North-East monsoon from December until it, in turn, blew itself out in March.

In the late seventeenth and early eighteenth century, English vessels in particular traded at the Chinese ports of Chusan, Lingpo and Amoy (and on occasions elsewhere); but the success of the *Macclesfield* during the 1699/1700 season at Canton made this the main port of trading from then onwards, although as late as 1755 other ports were occasionally visited for Private Trade or to meet cargoes that came from Japan. By 1760 the Emperor had expressly forbidden trading at ports other than Canton.

The Indiaman sailed up the Pearl River leaving Macao to its left and then through the Boca Tigris, where the river divided and narrowed, to the island of Whampoa, twelve miles below Canton, where it anchored. First, it was essential that the Chinese Customs 'measure' the ship in order to decide dues, a process which could sometimes be fraught with problems if the Chinese officials did not receive a fair commission. Then the supercargoes set sail in small 'chop' boats for the Company factories on the waterfront at Canton.

From the early eighteenth century until they were finally destroyed by fire in 1856, the factories, or foreign 'hongs' or warehouses, on the waterfront at Canton were the focus of all European mercantile activity in the China trade. Facing south towards Honam Island across the river and occupying an area about 350 yards broad and 100 yards deep, they consisted of thirteen buildings which ranged from plain European box-like structures with open forecourts between them and the river, to the elaborate porticoed building of the Hon. East India Company, with a broad verandah stretching almost to the water's edge. Each contained living quarters, a dining hall and numerous storerooms, while behind them was 'Thirteen Factory Street' and the busy thoroughfares of the walled city of Canton and in front, a teeming variety of small boats on the river. The hongs were made the subject of paintings by European and Chinese artists over almost a century, and from about 1765 to 1795 they were illustrated on numerous large porcelain punch bowls, which an American invoice of 1785 records as costing $5½ each.

News of the arrival of a ship quickly reached the Chinese merchants in Canton and they might sail at once to Whampoa to negotiate the purchasing of incoming cargo; alternatively, they would meet the supercargoes on their arrival in the city. At the start of each new season, the Chinese merchants were anxious to purchase so that they had European goods available before their rivals. This desire was tempered by the need to bargain a better price, and the feeling that it was perhaps more advantageous to wait for the arrival of further ships in case later cargoes were better suited to their requirements.

Supercargoes who had been to Canton before at once sought out the merchants with whom they had done successful business in the past, and before deciding on a price for selling would note the cost of Chinese goods for the new season and whether there was anything in short supply which they should buy at once. Since they were likely to be there for up to six months, they too were cautious about buying too quickly for fear that further supplies coming into Canton might lower the price later in the season. There are records of the Chinese merchants entertaining their European clients to dinner, and in this atmosphere of good will it seems certain that the reputation that a supercargo or Chinese merchant had gained in previous years was important in deciding the policy for that season and the trust which each placed in the other.

The supercargo would have to get suitable value for his silver and buy gold at a good price; more difficult were the negotiations over woollen and other cloth (sold by the yard) and cargoes of lead (sold by the 'picul' – a measure of about $133\frac{1}{3}$ lbs). When this seemed settled, the supercargo would draw up an agreement of sale in the form of a contract. In the case of the *Macclesfield* the cargo loaded in London with a value of £5,475 was finally sold in Canton for 36,000 taels – £12,000.

Only now was it possible to agree further purchases in Canton and here two main considerations had to be borne in mind – first: what orders from the Company, or private orders, had been given in London; and second: what was available in Canton and at what price.

As the pattern of trade developed over the years, the senior supercargoes were able to interpret the requests from the Directors in London in the light of what they found in Canton. But there were occasions when the Chinese, anticipating particularly heavy trading in some commodities, had very large supplies available and were anxious to sell quickly at an advantageous price, for fear of having stock left on their hands. The Company purchases of porcelain were a modest part of the cargo – in an average year between 5 per cent and 10 per cent by weight. Tea was the most important commodity and seldom comprised less than two-thirds of the cargo throughout the eighteenth century.

The orders from the Directors for each ship were in a standard form and those for the *Loyal Bliss* in 1712, for instance, appoint Mr Edward Fenwick as Chief Supercargo and John Child and Peter Godfrey as his juniors. After general instructions on avoiding hazards, they continue by giving the supercargoes a detailed list of commodities to be purchased. This commences:

Tea, Bohea, to be all the best procurable and none ordinary – 80,000 pounds

and continues with a list of other teas in various quantities. Much space is then given to 'Chinaware of the several sorts under mentioned vizt . . .' of which certain items are particularly interesting.

[item] 4 – Handle Chocolatettes of two sorts 20,000

(The sorts were 'blue & white of different flowers [&]

ditto smaller sort with brown edges' – Hogarth's engraving *The Countess's Morning Levée* of about 1740 shows the company drinking chocolate from cups without saucers.)

[item] 5 – Ditto in collours and gold . . . with gold edges & variety of patterns 20,000

[item] 6 – Milk Potts the largest coloured & gold 2,000
     ditto blue & white 2,000
     ditto second size . . . 2,000
     ditto third size . . . 2,000

[item] 7 – Milk Potts Glass pattern . . . 2,000 . . . .

[item] 9 – Plates in Collours and Gold with much scarlet, gold edge with varietey of patterns 10,000

(The last were clearly of Chinese Imari patterns.)

Later there are cups and saucers ordered separately – totalling 90,000 cups and 90,000 saucers, some described 'as painted after the Japan pattern'.

In all there are about 424,000 pieces ordered and before the instructions turn to 'China Raw Silk' there is the note:
If you can't get all the sorts of China ware or the full quantities of each sort above mentioned, get as many of them as you can. If you can't get the sorts exactly according to the Patterns get them as near as you can. If any Japan junks are at Canton while you are there which have Japan earthenware, you may buy some of the above sorts or pretty near them but buy none that are large Pieces such as Jars Beakers or great dishes or bowls . . . .

With such instructions and such quantities there was a great deal of latitude for the enterprising supercargo. Edward Fenwick, John Child and Peter Godfrey all included in their Private Trade exceptional armorial services for themselves – although almost certainly these were not shipped until the following year.

Indeed, as the summer turned to autumn in Canton and the supercargoes completed the unloading of the silver, lead and other cargoes and gathered and packed supplies in their factories or hongs, there was a great deal of opportunity both to choose for the Company, and to select some especially attractive patterns for their own Private Trade.

There was also special work to be done in agreeing patterns for later seasons. In the Company books is a record of a considerable payment of £28 for 'wooden models to be sent to China', and from the description these would appear to be for goblets with turned finials on the cover (probably similar to those found on the Chinese vessel of c.1695 salvaged off the coast of Vietnam and sold in 1992 at Christie's Amsterdam).

Later in the century it became the regular practice to

place large orders for the following season – but on occasion the ships then arriving were found to carry different or more up to date instructions from the Company. This was particularly difficult when, after 1760, merchants stayed on at the factories during the 'dead season' (after the last vessel had departed in March and before the earliest of the new season's ships arrived at the end of June). They might already have collected the supplies ordered and had these packed and ready for their arrival, only to find that occasionally (as in 1779) the Company ordered no porcelain at all that year.

Such problems did not arise with Private Trade, where decisions to purchase were made at the time and specially commissioned porcelain could not be cancelled without penalties and loss.

It is impossible to be specific about the degree of design choice available, but undoubtedly, if a particular pattern pleased the supercargoes, the Chinese would make more for the next season. Without doubt enterprising Chinese merchants who saw new designs delivered would themselves then order similar patterns with different borders, either to reduce cost, or to appeal to European merchants from other companies for the next season. Difficulties arose, however, where a wide variety of similar designs which did not quite match were on the market at the same time or were delivered together in response to large orders. The eventual retail demand in Europe for table ware would be in dinner or tea 'setts' and it was very important that plates matched dishes, salts, tureens and so on. Even with careful planning there would almost certainly be some pieces left over after sets were assembled; indeed the method of ordering cups, saucers, milk jugs and teapots all separately in bulk, and not as sets, was certain to lead to mismatches. This in turn led to the Company's reducing the number of patterns ordered – a policy that became increasingly restrictive as the century progressed, so that in 1774, for instance, only two design patterns were specified in orders for over a hundred thousand pieces of enamelled wares, and four for an even larger number of blue and white.

From the earliest days in Canton there had been considerable rivalry between merchants and sailors of different nations. The British distanced themselves particularly from any dealings with the Ostend Company, who were regarded as unreliable in Canton, and were thought to encourage smuggling of cargo from the Continent into England. There was always jealousy between the English and French, and while ordinary seamen might come to blows, the supercargoes were very anxious to arrive before the French – both to sell their European goods at the best price and to place orders quickly in Chinese shops before the best stock had been taken.

While the *Macclesfield* was loading in December 1699, the arrival of a Manila ship at Macao with at least 300,000 Spanish dollars to spend raised the price of raw and wrought silks considerably and caused the Chinese merchant Hunshunquin, who had bought English cloth, great difficulty in completing his contract with Mr Douglas, the British supercargo. The Chinese merchants preferred to sell their merchandise for dollars rather than bargain for English goods and first they asked to return cloth worth more than £6,000; when this was agreed they tried to negotiate a penal discount as well; alternatively, they wanted the British to pay much more for their silk than had originally been agreed. So fierce was the dispute that the *Macclesfield* did not sail until 21 July and only after the *hoppo* (the senior Chinese official) had himself purchased part of the cargo (at a favourable price). The *Macclesfield* had missed the monsoon and had to sail to Chusan where it traded with some success, leaving on 24 December 1700 and arriving off Portsmouth on 1 July 1701. Such a struggle was not typical of later journeys, but it illustrates the fierce bargaining necessary to secure success when trading with the Chinese.

An understanding gradually developed, however, between supercargoes of each nation and the Chinese merchants whom they found most helpful in Canton. In July 1723 four English ships reached Canton, the chief supercargo being William Fazakerley, assisted by Richard Morton, Edmund Godfrey, Thomas Carter, Thomas Dade, Devereux Bacon and Samuel Skinner (who was later killed by the pirate Angrea in a desperate battle off India in 1731). After two months of negotiation they signed a contract for the Company with Suqua on 3 September 1723 for the purchase of about 198,000 pieces of 'China Ware' at agreed prices.

Of these about 113,000 were plates and dishes, the principal designs being described as 'pale blue & white', 'dark blue & white' (together accounting for 76,000), 'gold & colours basket flower', 'gold & colours bamboo tree', and 'different col'rs Paddy, Bird & Deer'. There were also 70,000 cups and saucers with seven different descriptions, 'blue & white with birds', 'blue & white, diff't figure', etc. All the cups and saucers were blue and white and all also specified with 'brown rim'.

It must have transpired that more money was available, or that the prices were advantageous, for on

4 October a further contract was agreed with Quiqua for 21,900 extra dishes and bowls, while two days later a supplementary contract was agreed with Suqua for some expensive bowls of 'gold and colours . . . border & gold rim' – 300 nests of four.

It would be particularly interesting to know details of the private cargo that year, for the Company had regulated the trading by supercargoes only as recently as 1722 into 'Allowance', 'Permission' and 'Privilege' and the latter, which encompassed goods of the supercargoes' own choice, was probably about £1,000 in all. It is very likely, however, that Mr Godfrey, Mr Carter and Mr Skinner ordered armorial services, for porcelain with their arms is known of that date.

Similar contracts were agreed in subsequent years, and in 1734 the India Office records contain a Minute to the effect that 'We ordered Mr Scrivener to give us such a proportion for Setts of Dishes and Plates as would best suit the Traders in England . . .', and there is a letter dated 10 August 1734 from Canton which reads 'At a consultation, all present, we agreed to buy some China ware agreeable to the sortments delivered us by Mr. Scrivener, which we had seen att Emmanuel Quiqua's. Accordingly we sent for him and contracted with him for . . . .' The contract that follows totals 110,000 pieces (with cups and saucers counted separately) and is very largely blue and white porcelain, with 10,000 pieces described as 'enamelled' or 'painted' (these being the only three descriptions given).

Especially interesting is the footnote to the letter: 'All to be delivered immediately. The Setts of Dishes and Plates were made after the particular Direction of the French last Year & the blue and white especially seem to have had a good deal of care bestowed on them. We were the more anxious to secure this parcell as the Supracargoes of the French Ship are hourly expected at Canton, who therefore might else probably prevent us.' History does not relate what the French said on arrival.

The records of actual goods purchased by the supercargoes for themselves are, alas, scarce, but it is possible to deduce a considerable amount by default. Although further information may still be found, none of the records of Company purchases for the British market appear to include any of the finer birds and animals made from about 1735 onwards. No mention is made of porcelain copied after engravings or special designs, and no mention of special borders with portraits or buildings. The best known exception to this rule are the porcelains ordered between 1735 and 1740 by the Dutch East India Company with designs by Cornelis Pronk (most of which are illustrated in this book): but although this was a short-lived venture for the V.O.C. and undoubtedly ended because of the heavy cost of special designs set within unfamiliar borders, the Dutch company continued to be the more design conscious. Their records, quoted by Jörg, show that the V.O.C. ordered twenty-five boar's head and twenty-five goose tureens in 1763, and while a larger order in the following year was cancelled because the supercargoes felt it too risky, these were by no means the only larger figures ordered by the Dutch Company.

But while details are seldom given, a few exceptions arise where armorial porcelain is concerned. One of the most interesting concerns the cargo of Captain Gostlin of the Prince Augustus dated 20 December 1727 in Canton, shortly before the vessel sailed – '5 chests of China with the Arms of Lord King's and some other gentlemen'. This is a particularly revealing entry, for Lord King of Ockham had a service made for himself when he became a baron in the summer of 1725 and was made Lord Chancellor. The next sailing to China would have been early in 1726 and one would expect the service to have been ready by the autumn of 1727 – as indeed it was.

At the same time he ordered a service for his sister which has the same rim design. There are five other armorial services recorded with virtually the same border design as that of Lord King (Talbot, Sayer, Lethieullier and two for Frederick). Almost certainly the five chests contained some of these; there is also a Gostlin armorial service which may have sailed with Captain Gostlin on an earlier voyage, or may have been made for a relative who was a Director of the Company for twenty-nine years.

Mr John Scrivener, who was senior supercargo on the Sussex which arrived at Canton in 1737, shipped six boxes of chinaware. In the following season, Captain Charles Hudson (who later succeeded to his family baronetcy) gives details of his purchases in a letter from St Helena. His private cargo comprised 42 chests of Chinaware valued at £700, together with 'Lacquer'd ware 20 cases [£117]; Paper pictures, 2 boxes [£43] & Fans, two boxes [£50]'; while the supercargoes on the same ship, Prince of Orange, loaded 49 boxes and tubs of lacquered ware, pictures and porcelain (total value together about £280) together with 'Three boxes of China Ware containing dishes & plates & Tea setts with their Coats of Arms value [£54]', these last 'Directed to Jas. Colebrook and Jas. Buck Esq.' There is a Colebrook armorial dinner and tea service of exactly that date.

By the end of the century supercargoes, captains and officers of the English East India Company alone had purchased special commissions in Canton which included almost five thousand armorial services (about one a week for the century) as well as services for thirty City livery companies, at least twenty societies and two regiments; and mugs, punch bowls or plates for two inns, a breeches maker, a post office, a hat-maker, a boat-builder, a 'man-midwife' and 'George Harding, China Warehouse, No. 189 Minories' (in London). Of the vast majority there is no known contemporary record at all.

It is only possible to guess at the exact arrangements made by the supercargoes and captains when they brought these special commissions from England, but drawings and written instructions were carried from London, sometimes in the writing of the family concerned, and the resulting porcelain provides an intriguing glimpse of this. About 1740 a service was made for a London merchant, Calverley Bewicke, with his armorials. Each piece of the service was duly painted in China with 'Our coat of arms' in untidy script written beneath the armorials – clearly an instruction which the English merchant failed to explain to his Chinese counterpart in Canton, or which the latter failed to understand.

This illuminates the nature of the originals which changed hands in the china shops of Canton, and shows that errors were likely to be the fault of the European rather than the Chinaman, who copied what he was given. Some fifty years later, a tea service was made which appears to have combined the shield of the Earl of Stair and the crest, supporters, coronet and motto of John Crichton, Earl of Erne (before he was raised to that title in 1781). Undoubtedly a herald artist in Edinburgh or London had copied the armorials incorrectly, for no Chinese painter could have made such a mistake. No doubt too that the unfortunate supercargo lost much of his investment, for neither earl would have wanted it. It was almost certainly sold at auction, the teapot being acquired by a Doctor James Crichton, who was not closely related. Dr Crichton, a man of many parts, was, in fact, at the time a surgeon and trader in Canton, as well as being physician to the Governor-General of India.

Once the main orders had been placed, increased attention could be given to smaller special orders to take advantage of the 'Privilege' allowed by the Company. Visits to the china shops in the city are recorded on at least two porcelain tea services which show two or more foppishly dressed European merchants in discussion with Chinese shopkeepers,

their shelves behind loaded with jars and vases. The supercargoes and captains carried examples of the latest porcelain patterns from Europe to be copied, or drawings of their ships to be commemorated on porcelain. Prices were agreed, deposits paid, or exchanges made for clocks or watches and other 'novelties' from Europe.

There is a series of punch bowls decorated with a ship before and after a storm during the journey, and with different officers' names painted on the footrim of each bowl. It is clear that the actual handwriting of the amateur artist was faithfully copied. The ship *Haslingfield*, which nearly foundered in a hurricane in September 1743, is depicted '. . . in Prosperity Septbr. ye 11th 1743' and '. . . in distress Septbr. ye 12th 1743'. A distressing scene is shown with the masts and spars broken and floating overboard, and even the artist's name is given – 'Jams. Beech fecit'. There are other more whimsical and possibly 'standard' designs, with sea nymphs in their alluring nakedness seated on old wrecks.

Until after 1800 almost all the porcelain used for export was made at Jingdezhen, some five hundred miles north of Canton, and since, for most of the first half of the eighteenth century, all special orders were taken by Chinese merchants to the factories, there was no chance of these commissions being ready to sail in the same season. Clearly this delay led to difficulties, and by shortly after 1740 a number of decorating workshops had opened in Canton and on Honam Island on the other side of the river, enabling the china shops to promise a much faster delivery and to deal with the smaller orders that would only be placed if they could be ready to sail with the ship that brought them.

Whether some painters moved from Jingdezhen to Canton is not clear, but this seems probable, as there was little change in quality. During the 1740s and 1750s a very wide variety of European scenes copied from engravings and paintings were commissioned, with a range of more standardized, European-inspired borders which include Meissen-style gilding, scrolls, flower sprays and patterns taken from engravings *en grisaille*. For a time the larger orders were probably still painted at Jingdezhen, although by 1760 this was becoming less likely. It may be no coincidence that 1761 was the first year in which an English supercargo, Francis Wood, remained in Canton during the dead season to collate orders and prepare for the next season's ships, although the strain was obviously considerable, for he was invalided home during the autumn.

Before the end of the 1760s the border patterns for special orders and armorials, now more repetitive and usually of small sprays or standard garlands of flowers, were almost certainly painted in Canton workshops, and by 1770 there is evidence that these workshops were buying from Jingdezhen quantities of porcelain with underglaze blue borders, suitable for enamelling as orders came in. These underglaze borders could not be executed within the city for they required much higher temperature kilns, and Canton was always at risk from fire – the last major one having been in 1742, when sailors from Commodore Anson's squadron played a major part in saving the city from disaster.

This blue bordered ware in various designs was sent from Jingdezhen by river to Nanking and thence to Canton by sea; it was known to the Europeans as 'Nanking Chinaware' – a misleading term, for no porcelain was made there. Among the patterns available was one favoured by the newly appointed President of the Select Committee, Thomas Fitzhugh, a third generation East India supercargo and merchant who had in 1779 been appointed to this new Company post.

Thomas Fitzhugh had been specially appointed to tackle a particularly delicate problem, for during the 1770s very large credits had been built up by successful English supercargoes which it was now clear their Chinese counterparts were unable to settle. These credits totalled the enormous sum of almost £1 million, the total, however, being greatly swelled by compound interest – frequently charged at 18 per cent or 20 per cent – which had been allowed to accrue over a period of up to seven years.

When all the claims were collated and the Chinese merchants made it clear they could not pay, Thomas Fitzhugh approached the Governor of the Province who was both surprised and angered at the situation. Early in 1780 he replied to Fitzhugh that under an Edict of 1760 it was illegal to make loans to Chinese merchants and that any business transactions that attracted interest must be limited to an amount of interest less than the principal loan.

The English – for other countries with similar problems did not wish to press any claims for fear of repercussions – were amazed by the reply, for they had had no knowledge of the 1760 Edict; the supercargoes of that time had long departed and in any case none of them had understood sufficient Chinese to learn of such rules.

After very difficult negotiations, a solution was reached by September of that year which allowed interest up to a maximum of twice the principal, a small number of Chinese merchants were made bankrupt and all their business and private property was seized, and they were imprisoned and later banished. The Company, who had largely been acting for the supercargoes and had never themselves allowed more than one year's credit, were alarmed to find that from now onwards the Governor would appoint an official to oversee all negotiations with the English merchants, and that offered prices of teas had to be standardized; while a levy was placed on both imported and exported wares to pay for this organization and also for commissions for a number of Chinese mandarins.

The problem of debts continued to rumble on throughout the 1780s, for the Company's supercargoes were obliged to make large advances of up to 50 per cent on teas and 90 per cent on silk to enable the country dealers to supply them in time for the next season. This may not have affected the small Private Trade in porcelain, although undoubtedly advances were made when orders were placed, and although figures are not recorded, it could well have been between these levels.

On a number of occasions it seemed as if the worst fears of the Company were realized as supercargoes left the employ of the Company and became resident in Macao while acting as private merchants for independent trading vessels which called at Canton; and although orders were given that they should leave, some avoided this by becoming consuls for foreign governments and carrying on as before.

In the 1780s the Chinese authorities became particularly concerned by the increasing number of private trading vessels arriving at Canton without silver or piece goods but with cargoes of opium from India, and on occasion these were turned away without being allowed to trade. By 1800, however, it was clear to the Company that when such trading did take place it produced special commissions for the Chinese local officials, and although opium was officially banned from Company ships, the nineteenth century was to see this trade greatly enlarged until it resulted in the Opium Wars of the 1830s.

However, relations at this time between the Company supercargoes and the Chinese Hong merchants and officials were not always difficult, and in April 1783, before the English left their factory for the holiday season at Macao, they entertained fourteen important mandarins and a leading merchant to dinner who were reported to be 'extremely well pleased with the attention paid to them'.

Problems of policy required very careful attention

from the senior supercargoes in Canton, and sometimes also from the Governor-General in India or the Court of Directors in London. The volume of trade continued to grow with as many as twenty-nine ships·in Canton in both 1786 and 1787 on the Company's account alone, while the seasons continued to dictate that the months of December, January and February would see great activity on the river between Canton and Whampoa as the chop boats ferried cargo for loading.

By December, most of the porcelain was packed, often in sago – although third quality tea was also used. Some specially commissioned porcelain may have arrived at the last moment, for the large dinner service for John Chadwick had painted on the back of each piece 'Canton in China 24th January 1791'. The real ballast in the hold of an East Indiaman was usually made up of stones, but the porcelain made an excellent 'flooring' for the vessel and this was loaded first. There are earlier V.O.C. instructions (which would probably have applied also to English ships) that heavier plates and dishes should be loaded before teawares and hollow vases. (In the past this has given rise to the story that porcelain was 'bought for ballast'. It was, in fact, used for ballast to dispense with too much worthless weight being carried.) Above the porcelain were loaded the cheaper teas and then the more expensive, while silks and lacquerware and fans and spices were reserved until last.

There is evidence, too, that special boxes and barrels of private cargo were loaded last and even stored in officers' cabins. Certainly the private porcelain cargo recovered from the wreck of the Dutch ship *Geldermalsen*, which sank in 1752, was found in distressed condition scattered widely on the seabed: in marked contrast, the standard Company ware was recovered tightly packed in the hold and protected after the sinking by the cargo of tea which slowly sank round it, so that the glaze remained almost perfect.

When the last ships had sailed from Whampoa on their homeward voyage, and the last Chinese instructions had been observed, the Company officials and private merchants remaining at Canton took small boats to Macao to relax and enjoy a period of rest – and well might they need it.

# 4 The Auction

Because the Hon. East India Company offices and warehouse were in London, when returning East Indiamen berthed at Greenwich the supercargoes' accounts, including records of the Private Trade, left at once for East India House, while all cargo was unloaded and stored in the Company's warehouses, with the exception of a very small number of personal gifts and on some occasions armorial services.

In the early eighteenth century the Customs assessed the listed value for duty at 17 per cent and the Company assessed freight and handling at about 15 per cent. It was noted in Court minutes of 1711 that measures against smuggling must be strengthened and there are references in the Customs House records at Greenwich to small amounts of porcelain being seized. Checks were made to ensure that officers' free carriage allowances were not exceeded, and another minute of 1711 recorded that one 'allowance' of £1,300 had actually realized £19,000 at auction!

From the 1670s until the nineteenth century, the great majority of the cargoes – indeed originally it had been intended that all cargo – was auctioned so that a final balance could be struck and accounts cleared on each venture. In this way the capital invested at the outset could be compared with the total result of the auction, and accounts could be settled as soon as practicable to the benefit of those who had invested. If any exceptions were made, they would have concerned servants of the Company, who would settle payments direct. The results would then be reflected in the accounts of the Hon. East India Company, a joint stock company which declared a dividend (usually annually) and whose shares were available on the open market. As far as Private Trade in porcelain was concerned, this was, until the late eighteenth century, only a small part of the total porcelain purchased – itself likely to have been less than ten per cent of any ship's cargo.

It was always some months before an auction was held and unfortunately auction records are preserved only from between 1685 and 1709 (1696 is the first year in which a wide range of shapes is described) and again for 1722; in that year 625,000 pieces of porcelain were sold in the March sale from cargoes of the previous season; also some from earlier seasons that had been held over because of a glut on the market.

These records provide the most accurate details of what was offered both by the Company and the Private Trade – but details of many later years can be gauged from the supercargoes' diaries which exist from 1722 until the end of the eighteenth century, although with a few years missing and a gap from 1753 to 1775. There is no evidence that either the size or frequency of the auctions altered much until the end of the century.

Through their auctions the Company controlled the whole market and they did not allow any other avenues of Private Trade. Their early policy of not allowing china merchants to place orders with supercargoes for delivery direct to the merchants was designed to ensure that they received auction commission on all goods, and that supercargoes could not be tempted to put the interests of Private Trade before that of the Company. There is little doubt, however, that captains and other officers were privy to the requirements of china dealers and in some cases shops, and were able to buy carefully what was wanted in Canton so that the best prices could be obtained in London.

At the auction anyone could purchase any lot, and merchants, supercargoes, captains or crew would bid for the lots that they had financed and brought to England and, after payment, take the lot for whatever purpose they wished. Clearly, if they were already owners of a lot, the net cost of this would only be the auction commission to the East India Company. Once repossessed the porcelain could either be sold privately, perhaps to a china shop, on the basis of this established market price, or kept for private use.

Sale catalogues were issued giving reserve prices, and while the Company's lots were large and of one type (lots of 1,000 cups or 2,000 bowls were not uncommon and in 1710 180,000 cups and saucers and 45,000 'coarse cups' were put up in one sale), many of the private lots were small, some belonging to ordinary seamen, and teapots, saucers, cups and plates could all be included in one lot. There were no 'estimates', only 'reserves'.

The reserves were shown separately against each type of porcelain and thus there could be three or four reserves for different types all in one lot. When lots

with one type only were sold, prices were 'per each' in
the lot and thus 160 teapots are recorded as 'sold at 5
shillings each'. When, however, mixed lots were sold,
they were at an 'advance on the reserves': thus in one
lot in 1706 '11 Long necked bottles red on gold,
reserve 10s, 3 Brownd hubblebubbles reserve 6s, 1
ditto chipped, reserve 5s' were together 'sold at 11s
advance' presumably, on the whole lot.

In spite of their control of the trade, the bulk buying
of porcelain by the Company proved over the years to
be no match for the individual initiative of the Private
Traders. The Directors would seem to have been
scarcely aware of this and it was not in the interests of
the supercargoes and captains to tell them, but
undoubtedly this situation existed throughout the
century. A letter of 1790 from London to Canton reads

. . . if you had been led to believe . . . . that the Private
Trade china-ware is in general inferior to that of the
Company's you have shewn yourselves possessed but of little
knowledge, as the fact is notoriously the reverse . . . we have
an opportunity of knowing this by actual comparisons as
both sorts go through the same channel of our sales and even
the selling prices would prove the fact, if we had no other
way of judging.

In December 1696, the cargo of the *Dorothy* was the
first for which an itemized list is known (earlier
auctions, for the most part, listing only crates or boxes
of porcelain), but the descriptions are even then not
particularly revealing, as such words as 'fine', 'little',
'painted' and 'blewish colour' are used; all 96,000 pieces
were tea wares offered on behalf of the Company.

In 1703 a large cargo was not sold because too much
was available and the Company was anxious that prices
should show a good return.

The cargo of the *Union*, sold in March 1705,
comprised 182,895 pieces of porcelain and a much
wider choice from Company purchases including
'punch bowls', 'flasks', 'bottles', 'rosewater bottles' and
'essence bottles'. These pieces achieved a total of
£10,609 – averaging approximately 14d per piece sold;
£790 was recorded as being unsold, and if lots failed to
reach their reserve, goods were automatically put back
for the next auction.

The catalogue of the *Aurengzeb* cargo, sold in
September 1705, prefaces the porcelain lots with terms
which would be familiar today:

Lots to be seen at the East India House

49 lots – to be taken with all faults

no allowance to be made on any lot on pretence of not
answering the sample . . .

The Company will not allow ringing [whether meaning the
practice of tapping porcelain to test for cracks or the bidding
by one buyer on behalf of others, is not clear]

These terms indicate that a good deal had to be
taken on trust, for where a lot contained several
hundred teapots in cases, only samples were shown and
damage had to be assessed without viewing – perhaps
occasionally on inside information from the porters.
The situation with private cargo was even more risky,
for lots were packed in 'barrels' with a list of what they
contained, and the porcelain on top, if damaged, could
easily give the appearance of being a poor lot; which
could, for example, enable the officer concerned to
buy cheaply or at cost and thus reduce the Company's
commission.

In April 1706, the cargo of the *Kent* was sold but no
Company porcelain was offered because, as a result of
the 1703 glut, orders had been given to buy little for
the Company in Canton in 1705. All the porcelain
offered was private.

Private cargo was shown in the auction catalogues
with the initials of its owner; this made it easier for a
china merchant to identify a particular lot or barrel
(which might even have been purchased with him in
mind), but because of the uncertainty of the contents
of the barrels, there was a need for 'inside knowledge'.
An example of this is the private cargo purchased in
Canton by 'G.T.' of the *Carnarvon* in 1720 (the captain
was Josiah Thwaites and it may have been him) which,
when auctioned in March 1722, was bought almost
exclusively by a Mr Lane for what was considered a
low price (although without breakages or quality being
known, that is even more difficult to assess today than
it was at the time). In fact, 'G.T.' received £162 gross
for 1,320 pieces (averaging 29½d each) – which
included 'large blue and white garden pots'
('jardinières' or garden seats) and coffee pots – and it
can only remain a suspicion that the real contents of his
unexamined barrels was already known to Mr Lane.

This and similar incidents led the Court of Directors
to set up an enquiry in 1722 under the chairmanship of
Sir Matthew Decker, a very successful Anglo-Dutch
merchant, created a baronet in 1716, who was well
aware of the realities of the trade, and had had two fine
armorial services from China delivered a few years
earlier. In a minute of 11 January 1723 the enquiry
concluded that '. . . any goods in Private Trade
[should] be fairly exposed to the view of the buyers
and sold to the highest bidder in the same manner as
the Company's goods are . . .'.

The major sale of Company wares in March 1722 is

The sale room at India House; engraving, 1808

as revealing of the buyers as it is of the porcelain sold. All appear to have been wholesale china merchants, who also bought lacquer and fans, and whose main market would have been the china shops in London and the provinces – although some merchants were also shareholders in shops. As with much else in the trade, the lines were blurred.

In all, 43 merchants are recorded as spending £34,000 on about 625,000 pieces – a lower average price than at the sale in 1705, but the market was clouded by the scandal of the 'South Sea Bubble' and by some smuggling of goods previously sold at auctions of the Ostend Company. (It is of interest, but not especially instructive, to compare this with the £10 million spent on 172,000 pieces of porcelain in 1986 when the cargo of the *Geldermalsen*, sunk in 1752, was auctioned in Amsterdam.)

Of the buyers in March 1722, four spent more than £1,000 – Mr Daniel King, £4,874; Mr Akerman,

£2,192; Mr Lane, £1,515; and Mr John Ferguson, £1,036. Other principal purchasers were Tombs, Margas, Barnes, Sibley, Stanton and Durden. Clearly Mr King overbought in a falling market for on 6 November 1722 the *London Gazette* reports that a Petition for Bankruptcy had been brought against Mr Daniel King, Chinaman, of Fenchurch Street.

A wholesale china merchant depended greatly on his customers once he had bought at auction, and Mr Daniel King is known to have had a share of the more unpredictable re-export trade between 1719 and 1722. He is recorded as shipping porcelain and fans to Cork in Ireland, Amsterdam, Rotterdam, Madeira, Gibraltar, New England and Barbados; and by doing this he was able to recover the 17 per cent duty that had been paid on importing the goods. Contemporary records show that New York, Philadelphia, Baltimore and Boston were the most likely destinations in America at that time, and that about 1 per cent of the porcelain in the

1722 auction was re-exported there.

After 1722 it is only possible to follow what happened at auctions through minutes of the Court of Directors, supercargoes' diaries and other similar references, but it is clear that the Company maintained a close, if pragmatic control on the market.

There are references to overdue accounts at auction when, for example, buyers were given until January 1732 to pay for purchases in the March 1731 sale. There are many references to the volume of the Private Trade, which always troubled the Company, but which at least provided revenue from commissions at little risk. Thus in 1733 officers were allowed to import up to £2,500 at auction price on condition that, if this sum was exceeded, an additional commission of 15 per cent would be charged. This was a virtual invitation to trade on any scale they chose if they considered it worthwhile.

It was not permitted to bring back Chinese porcelain privately on Indiamen returning from India, but if one had the right contacts or relations, porcelain could be carried on men-of-war. The Duke of Bedford had two boxes of chinaware shipped on the *Rainbow* in 1753 and paid a total of 16s 2d in charges. This may well have been the armorial service bearing the Duke's arms as they were after he became a Knight of the Garter in 1749, which is known to have arrived damaged. (It is thought that it lay for some generations unused, so bad was the damage and so upset the Duke when he saw it.)

It would seem that while the original intention, evident in the records of earlier auctions, was that *all* private trade had to be auctioned (an intention formed before the first armorial service was made), where armorial porcelain was concerned it became impractical to do this as the volume increased. No one other than the family for whom a service was made had the right to use the arms (indeed in Scotland anyone who used objects with the arms of a clan chief without authority could have them seized without compensation). Far better, then, for the Company to assess its value and raise duties and commissions on that.

The invoice of the blue and white Peers service already mentioned is dated 19 November 1731, Canton, and it was consigned by the ship *Canton Merchant* to Madras and thence on to London. Mr Charles Peers is known to have sailed on this ship from Madras and besides bringing this service home, he carried with him sets of Chinese mother-of-pearl counters, one of which had the armorials of his sister Sarah, which he gave to her on his arrival. Another service in *famille rose* with the arms of his father, Sir Charles Peers, a former Lord Mayor of London, had

arrived earlier in England direct from China, invoiced on 10 December 1731 and carried by Captain Samuel Martin on the ship *Harrison*. Both are invoiced in Chinese taels, the documents marked 'duplicate'. The Colebrook armorial services mentioned in the previous chapter were also 'directed to James Colebrook . . .' by the supercargoes on the *Prince of Wales* in 1739 and not to the Company.

The Okeover service seems to confirm this pattern, for it is invoiced in English currency for the account of Leake Okeover Esq. by Captain Ralph Congreve on 18 January 1740. The total for 70 plates and 30 dishes is £84 to which is added £4 for boxes and, significantly, 'King and Companys Duteys for 69 plates £11 11s' (no explanation is given as to why there is no duty shown on the dishes). In 1743 a second consignment of this most elaborate service was made, and the invoice is 'from ye Jerusalem Coffee House, Change Alley, a consignment of fifty plates and four dishes', signed by Captain Joseph Congreve of the ship *Prislowe*. The fact that the Peers and Okeover families still have these invoices almost certainly means that the porcelain was not put through the process of auction, but that they paid the sums mentioned, plus duty and agreed commission and other charges.

Nevertheless, there are two Court minutes, the first of 12 November 1731, which at first seem to tell a different story: 'Ordered that the Chinese ware with coats of arms etc and some white goods for presents, be put up to sale on Tuesday 23rd instance and that notice thereof be given accordingly.' And another, which may provide the answer, 'Ordered that the warehouse keeper of Private Trade do prepare some china ware, such and other small things belonging to General Diemar, which were brought home on the China ship to be put up at the same time with other Private Trade at this sale as soon as conveniently maybe, *in order that the same may be sent abroad to him*' [my italics.].

This minute suggests that the service was already consigned to General Diemar and that a question of valuation had to be decided, perhaps because some disagreement arose over charges or duty or even payment, so that chinaman wholesalers could place a valuation on the goods. In the case of the armorial service there must have been occasions, with such services averaging fifty a year, when the person who had ordered it was no longer alive – or when the arms indicated a marriage which never took place.

This does not mean that special consignments of porcelain with topical or other special designs would not have been auctioned, but even in this case there is no actual evidence for the period 1740 onwards –

when this type of design was most popular – and it would be unsafe to assume that what was done in 1705 still held in every case in 1745. One has to wonder in the case of a specially commissioned political or religious scene what the consequence would be of auctioning a special order requested by one chinaman with a particular market in mind. Either the type of subterfuge revealed in the minutes of 1723, or something similar, would have been employed. Again, an assessment, particularly if at a higher rate, would have been preferable.

Before 1700 the principal buyers at auction were general wholesale merchants who included chinaware amongst the other goods they bought and sold on to provincial distributors, retailers and for export. The Glass-Sellers' Company had a monopoly on the sale of both glass and pottery within seven miles of London, but although chinaware was not covered by the monopoly, many of these merchants expanded into that field.

In the early eighteenth century a new breed of chinamen established themselves – a prominent example being Peter Motteux, a Huguenot, who had earlier published a translation of *Don Quixote* and in an article in the *Spectator* in 1712 termed himself 'an author turned dealer', while mentioning his warehouse in Leadenhall Street with goods of the 'India and China Trade'. He had bought porcelain at auction as early as 1704, and his son became an eminent Hamburg merchant for whom the Motteux armorial service was probably made in the 1740s.

Another prominent and successful London merchant family from Brabant were the Lethieuliers, of whom John Lethieulier was a merchant buyer of porcelain whose cousins included a director of the Bank and a director of the East India Company. His immediate family had at least six armorial services made in the 1720s.

Some wholesalers developed their warehouses into shops where a fashionable clientele could buy not only porcelain but silks and lacquerware, mirrors and other oriental goods, including teas which, with tea sets, made up a substantial part of their business. A glimpse of this world is contained in the 1721 probate inventory of Joshua Bagshaw, a gentleman who became a prominent merchant and shop owner. His debtors' list included the Duchesses of Norfolk, Devonshire and Cleveland, the Duke of Bolton and the Earls or Countesses of Rockingham, Coningsby, Rochester and Stamford as well as Lord Castlemaine, Mr Samuel Pitt and Mrs Lewis of Bath and many other Society names. (No-one in the list, however, had an armorial service at that time; another indication that these were either paid for in advance, or directly to the Company.)

Although it was perhaps officially discouraged by Company regulations, it was probable that private clients would meet a supercargo in a warehouse or shop to explain their exact requirements. A number of wholesale merchants specializing in the India and China Trade sent their sons or apprentices out as supercargoes or assistants to gain experience. Mr John Scrivener, the son of a carpenter in Peckham, whose presence at a consultation in Canton in 1734 when china was bought from Emmanuel Quiqua has already been mentioned (and who later returned to Canton as Chief Supercargo in 1737), had just completed his apprenticeship to the well known chinaman John Akerman when he sailed on the *Harrison* as an assistant 'having Judgement in Tea and Chinaware'. Morse comments that 'his opinion on tea was sometimes accepted by the supercargoes and sometimes not; but on chinaware it was listened to with respect.' While Mr Scrivener was employed by the Company in 1734 and was allowed a 'Privilege' of just £50 for Private Trade, the experience he gained was certain to have been of great use in his later partnership of Akerman & Scrivener, who became one of the leading dealers in chinaware and cut glass. He was made a Freeman of the Glass-Sellers' Company in 1735, of which Company he was Master in 1754.

In spite of the Company's policy of keeping Private Trade within careful limits, it is evident that the volume increased as the century wore on. The allowances had been increased and dunnage could be filled privately (provided an extra 15 per cent commission was paid) and as Morse comments, 'restrictions placed from time to time on the private ventures of captains and officers were not long retained.' There were even years in which no Company porcelain was shipped home and the ships relied on the Private Trade of captains or supercargoes to floor the vessel.

It is now impossible to gauge how much of the finer Private Trade in porcelain, particularly armorial ware, was ordered by clients directly from captains or supercargoes and how much was ordered in London china shops, which then placed the commissions with these officers. It is, however, evident that the standard nature of the shields and mantling of many of the armorials from the 1760s onwards indicates that an organization was used by these shops (perhaps an office of unofficial herald painters who may have also undertaken other design work) which could translate customers' details of their arms into standard drawings, which were then taken to China.

In particular, the floral mantling of arms with two crossed scrolls beneath the shield was not a pattern adopted on silver or produced by the College of Arms on grants or paintings. It is confined to Chinese armorial porcelain for the British market, and at least seventy such armorial services were painted between 1755 and 1770; after which the fashion changed. In the 1780s and '90s an even larger number of services featured blue tasselled mantling about spade-shaped shields containing initials or armorials. Such a style was not unknown on other objects, but it is apparent that artists working for the chinamen filled in shields of a standard shape with details supplied by the family.

Where greater originality was required bookplates and engravings from reference books might be used, but considering the numbers of more standard designs, it would seem that by the third quarter of the century, the majority of armorial services were ordered through the retail trade. Coincidental with this was the production of pictorial designs, usually after popular prints, which employed border designs matching those on armorial porcelain of the same period. One exceptional service of about 1785 which countered the general trend employed different engravings and drawings of country houses and rural scenes on each piece, all with the crest of the Slater family, and it is clear that occasionally special commissions would include special instructions of this kind.

However, increasing standardization eventually played into the hands of the English porcelain manufacturers in Staffordshire and at Worcester who were willing to produce finer and more elaborate armorial services, often based on earlier Chinese designs. At their pleading, duties on the imported ware rose dramatically to 50 per cent in 1790 and over 100 per cent by 1800. Porcelain was, perhaps, the only manufactured Chinese product where comparable ware could be made in Europe, and it was inevitable that it should be singled out for retaliatory treatment by European governments under pressure from their own manufacturers to protect their fledgling industries.

The reaction of the East India Company in London was that it was no longer worthwhile putting even five per cent of the Company capital into Chinese porcelain (the percentage was no higher than this by 1790), and in 1791 they decided to stop importing Chinese porcelain altogether on their own account. However,

in spite of orders to this effect being sent to Canton in 1792, the volume of manufacturing was not so easily stemmed, nor were the American and other merchants there able to take up all that then became available. It was reported to London in 1795 that there was still about £20,000 worth of standard wares available and that this could be had at a discount of 15 per cent or at 'whatever price they may think proper'.

In London the china dealers had realized that a large part of their standard everyday trade had effectively ceased, and in spite of protests to the Company, their only source of supply in future was to be the Private Trade. The Company even advanced the opinion that it was possible to floor vessels without porcelain, something that had been taken to be essential for over a century, but in the exchange of arguments at the time this was not taken seriously.

Undoubtedly the Private Trade took careful note of the situation; and as the price advantage of Chinese wares evaporated and fashion swung to European wares, London china shops themselves ordered less from Canton and more from English factories. During the first decade of the nineteenth century the number of British ships clearing Canton for foreign destinations declined from 40 out of a total of 69 (with 23 American) in 1800, to 34 out of 49 (with 15 American) in 1810. But the volume of chinaware still imported by the Private Trade into England remained remarkably steady, and was recorded in Milburn's *Oriental Commerce*, published in 1813, as ranging from £268,701 in 1800 to £353,418 in 1810 (with the smallest and greatest annual amounts being £238,122 and £476,621 in 1807/8 and 1808/9 – presumably one compensating for the other).

Chinaware continued to be imported into England throughout the nineteenth century through private trading but in increasingly small quantities, and for much of the century it is probable that a larger volume sailed to America which had no substantial porcelain manufacturers of its own. By 1850 the British trade in Chinese porcelain was of little importance and only moderate in quality – in 1855 up to six times as much porcelain was imported from France as from Canton and in 1895 fifteen times as much came from Japan as from China. The total importation of Chinese porcelain into Britain in 1900 was less than 77 tons – less even than could have been carried on one East Indiaman in the eighteenth century at the height of the trade.

# The Porcelain

1550–1880

# The Dinner Service: Plates and Dishes

Examples, c.1550–c.1880

Plates and dishes have always been made both for use and display. Such was the quality of many, in the first half of the 18th century in particular, that some which were designed for use as part of dinner services were instead displayed in cabinets, almost from their arrival in the West.

Others were undoubtedly designed from the beginning for display – particularly those of eggshell quality or great size, of political significance, or erotic charm. It is clear that the great majority of these were ordered specially by the supercargoes for Private Trade.

I

# Dish

Jiajing, c.1550
Diameter: 11¾ in (29.9 cm)

Decorated in underglaze blue with rim of flowering branches and birds, the centre with an alert hare beneath a tree within a sketchy scroll band. The reverse decorated with five galloping horses in roundels and in the centre a linear scroll.

This is one of many designs on Ming dishes of this type made in the 16th century, the rims ranging from careful formal scrollwork to floral sprays and the centres including floral, aquatic and woodland designs with deer and birds, elephants and Chinese animals, pagodas, landscapes and riverscapes.

Such dishes were collected by Arab and Turkish officials throughout the Middle East and were to be bought

from merchants who had trade, probably overland, with China.

LITERATURE
Krahl & Ayers, *Chinese Ceramics in the Topkapi Saray Museum, Istanbul*, vol. II, p. 607 where a dish with almost exactly the same scene and similar reverse is illustrated.

# 3
# Dish

Chongzhen, c.1643
Diameter: $11\frac{1}{2}$ in (29.2 cm)

Decorated in underglaze blue and with glaze slightly worn from immersion, this late Ming dish was salvaged in 1983 by Captain Michael Hatcher from the wreck of a Chinese trading vessel.

The dating is possible because two of the 22,000 pieces recovered had the Chinese cyclical date for 1643. This is a late example of the panelled porcelain with a wide variety of central scenes, known as 'Kraakware', which had been popular for almost fifty years.

In 1643, however, cargoes were unreliable and merchants bought a wide variety of porcelain, much of it brought direct to Batavia by Chinese junks, as was intended in this case. The Ming Dynasty fell in 1644 and for about thirty years supplies of Chinese porcelain remained irregular or unavailable, giving the Japanese an opportunity to enter the market which they did with great success until the early years of the 18th century, by which time the shorter journey and plentiful supplies from Canton made their trade much less economic.

LITERATURE
Sheaf & Kilburn, *The Hatcher Porcelain Cargoes*, pp. 33, 34, 39, 40, 44 where a wide variety of Kraakware is illustrated.
Rinaldi, *Kraak Porcelain*, p. 209 where dating and this cargo are discussed.

# 2
# Dish

Wanli, c.1600
Diameter: $16\frac{1}{4}$ in (41.3 cm)

Of coarse porcelain in saucer shape painted in a dark inky blue, this dish is of a type now known as 'Swatow ware'. The design appears to suggest a compass encircled by two ships and hilly islands with a rim of primitive lattice work divided by four cartouches with stylized floral panels.

The name 'Swatow ware' derived from the port of export (situated in Guangdong Province at the mouth of the Han River) in rather the same way that Imari gave its name to porcelain manufactured inland and exported from Imari. The ware was provincial and little was shipped to Europe, so that what found its way there probably came via Batavia or India.

LITERATURE
Harrison, *Swatow*, pp. 79–80.
Howard & Ayers, *China for the West*, p. 52.

## 4
## Dish

Japanese, c.1670
Diameter: 14¼ in (36.6 cm)

Decorated with broad free wash strokes in underglaze purplish blue, with the central initials surrounded by two long-tailed birds and six border panels with plants on the rim.

The initials V.O.C. are those of the 'Vereenigde Oostindische Compagnie' – the Dutch East India Company, formed in 1602.

After the fall of the Ming Dynasty much of the porcelain trade was with Japan, and such dishes were produced there between about 1658 and the early 1680s, after Chinese originals of the early part of the 17th century – clearly showing the influence of Kraakware designs.

Many of these dishes were for use in the Company's stations at Batavia, Surat and elsewhere, but others were brought back for sale in Europe.

LITERATURE
Rinaldi, *Kraak Porcelain*, p. 226.
Ayers, Impey & Mallet, *Porcelain for Palaces*, p. 94 where another V.O.C. dish is also illustrated.

## 6
## Dish

Kangxi, c.1700
Diameter: $13\frac{3}{8}$ in (33.8 cm)

Decorated in underglaze blue with a European scene of musicians within eight petal-shaped panels with Chinese land and riverscapes.

This is one of the earliest examples of the use of an identified European print – 'The Music Party' drawn by Robert Bonnart and engraved by his brother Nicholas Bonnart (1646–1718).

This engraving was probably carried privately by a supercargo for there is no record at the time of any company using such engravings. It is more likely that this dish was prepared for the Dutch or French markets than for the English.

LITERATURE
Howard & Ayers, *China for the West*, p. 77 where the original engraving is also illustrated.

## 5
## Dish or Tray

Kangxi, c.1695
Diameter: $14\frac{1}{2}$ in (36.9 cm)

Heavily potted with narrow moulded and gadrooned rim and flat surface, decorated in underglaze blue within a circular panel with a vine-clad Bacchus standing on a tiled floor between a table with flask and goblet and a large wine jar; in the background a leaded window. About this is boldly painted formal scrollwork of vines and grapes.

The shape of this dish suggests a tray suitable for wine goblets. The tiled floor is particularly reminiscent of delftware and the scene probably derives from an engraving which has not so far been identified. Almost certainly originally for the Dutch market.

LITERATURE
Howard & Ayers, *China for the West*, p. 76.

# 7
# Deep dish

Kangxi, c.1700
Diameter: 13½ in (34.2 cm)

Decorated in underglaze blue with a central scene within a wide border of trellis work and eight cartouches, each with a lady holding a fan while another picks flowers. A six-character mark of Kangxi is unusual on export ware and may denote that some pieces were also intended for the Chinese market.

The central scene is after a European print illustrating the genteel pastime of guessing the names of flowers from their scent. It may be one of a series illustrating the sense of smell. The man's wig and the ladies' hair *à la mode Fontanges* date the original print to shortly before 1700.

The existence of a simplified version on small deep plates indicates the popularity of the subject.

LITERATURE
Beurdeley, *Porcelain of the East India Companies*, fig. 12.
Howard & Ayers, *China for the West*, p. 78.

8
Plate

Kangxi, c.1700
Diameter: $10\frac{1}{4}$ in (26 cm)

With shaped rim, decorated solely
in underglaze blue within a formal
border of lotus-and-cloud
scrollwork. Six-character mark of
Chenghua.

This hunting scene is one of a
number similar, usually illustrating
ladies armed with bows riding with
hounds after hares – some of which
may escape while others do not.
This Amazonian pursuit made such
sets of plates a favourite design over
more than a decade.

The Chenghua mark (1465–87) was
not intended as a forgery, but rather
as a compliment to the quality of
the piece and to replace the mark of
Kangxi who had forbidden the use
of his name on porcelain made for
export after 1682; a ban which
nominally remained in force until
the late 19th century.

## 9
## Two Saucer Dishes

Kangxi, c.1700
Diameter: 8½ in (21.6 cm)

Part of a set of six, all in underglaze
blue. The wavy rims decorated with
heavy diaper and petal moulding,
and painted with Buddhist symbols
enclosing multi-lobed panels, each
with a different scene of love-
making. On the reverse the
six-character mark of Chenghua.

These are finely painted examples
of the erotic art in which the
Chinese excelled and for which
there was a ready market in the
West. The 1643 Hatcher cargo
included sets of three beakers with
various stages of love-making.
Many such scenes, as in this case,
include a voyeur.

There are well known examples in
*famille verte* and later in *famille rose*,
and it is clear that some merchants
held a small discreet stock of such
pieces for private clients.

LITERATURE
Beurdeley, *Chinese Erotic Art*
illustrates a Kangxi beaker, p. 119,
and Qianlong perfume burners in
*famille rose*, p. 123.

## 10
# Plate

Kangxi, c.1700
Diameter: 6¾ in (17.2 cm)

Octagonal, decorated solely in underglaze blue with panelled borders and a crowded central motif combining two designs.

The spray of asters in the upper half of the central design is exactly as painted on cups and saucers of c.1695, recovered off the Vung Tau peninsula from the wreck of a Chinese vessel sailing to Batavia. The lower half of the design is well known in Holland as the 'cuckoo on the house'.

This design, the origin of which has never been fully explained, shows a small house and a separate tall chimney (on which occasionally sits a monkey) while two partridge-like birds fly in the sky.

There are a number of variations and the popularity of the design ensured its reordering over a considerable period.

## 11
# Plate

Kangxi, c.1700–20
Diameter: 7¾ in (19.7 cm)

With narrow crimped rim and decorated solely in underglaze blue; depicting a Dutch marsh and coastal scene, with figures and cows and the sails of ships anchored near houses on the horizon.

This design, almost certainly copied from a drawing by Frederick van Frytom (1652–1702), was obviously popular, for there are a number of variations, some with narrower rim and others made in Japan. It was possibly reordered over two decades by the Dutch company.

The rim design is unique in Chinese export porcelain and is almost certainly after a silver original. The scene was formerly (and incorrectly) thought to be Deshima Island in Nagasaki Bay where the Dutch had their Japanese 'factory', but is more recently considered to be near Scheveningen in Holland.

LITERATURE
Le Corbeiller, *China Trade Porcelain*, p. 29.
Howard & Ayers, *China for the West*, pp. 72–3 where two other versions are illustrated.

12

Dish

Kangxi, c.1705
Diameter: 13¾ in (34.9 cm)

Decorated in underglaze blue with a
central pheasant on rockwork; the
rim with stylized flowers and
scrollwork enclosing an armorial.

This is of Pelgrans, although the
oriental figure as crest is not
recorded. Such dishes are known
without the armorial and in this case
the arms replace a shaped floral
panel.

Jacob Pelgrans, a director of the
V.O.C., was resident in Bengal
from 1702 to 1708 and died in
Batavia in 1713. It seems likely that
he ordered the service while in
India and this may well account for
the amateur-like drawing of the
arms.

LITERATURE
Le Corbeiller, *Patterns of Exchange*,
p. 25.
Howard & Ayers, *China for the
West*, p. 82.

## 14
## Dish

Kangxi, c.1710
Diameter: 13 in (33 cm)

Of octagonal shape, with flaring sides decorated in the manner of Japanese ware with panels in Imari palette and scrollwork on an underglaze blue background. In the centre, beneath a red scroll, an armorial in underglaze blue and gold.

Underglaze blue ware, over-decorated in iron-red and gilding, was one of the palettes first developed in Japan and shipped from the port of Imari to the Dutch trading post at Deshima, and thence to Europe. These designs became known as 'Imari', but will be referred to here as 'Japanese Imari'. The popularity of this palette in Europe soon ensured that the Chinese copied many of the designs (the instructions in 1712 for the *Loyal Bliss* make this clear – see chapter 3), and such ware is usually referred to now as 'Imari' or 'Chinese Imari'.

The word 'Corbeau' on the scroll is the name of the family, for in French it means 'crow' and the arms of the French families of Corbel of Brittany and Corbet of Normandy have three crows, although correctly black on a white or gold ground. But the exact branch of the family is not clear.

This essentially Japanese design was later copied at Meissen.

LITERATURE
Howard & Ayers, *China for the West*, p. 141.
Rückert, *Meissener Porzellan 1710–1810*, cat. 316.

## 13
## Dish

Kangxi, c.1710
Diameter: 10⅝ in (27.1 cm)

Decorated in underglaze blue, this Chinese dish imitates the Japanese in style. The rim, divided into six panels – three with diaper and three with boys in floral scrollwork – encloses a boldly painted European merchant ship under full sail. The reverse with three flower sprays.

Although the ship is stylized, it is painted with considerable clarity and more in the manner of similar ships on Japanese Imari bowls of this period than on Chinese porcelain.

The comparative rarity of this design suggests an initiative by a private trader with experience of Japan, rather than an order from the Dutch East India Company itself.

## 15
## Plate

Kangxi, c.1710–15
Diameter: 10½ in (26.7 cm)

Decorated in underglaze blue in imitation of delftware, with five figures strolling among trees, and buildings on the horizon – probably church spires.

This is very similar to another plate of the same size in the Mottahedeh Collection and although the original could be Dutch delftware, it could equally be Lambeth delft; a scene with very similar trees and ecclesiastical and other buildings but with four figures was sold at Phillips, London in 1980 as 'probably Lambeth, c.1700–1710'. Such an original would have been taken to China for copying – probably for the Private Trade.

LITERATURE
Howard & Ayers, *China for the West*, p. 84 where the plate illustrated was marked 'N=499' and formerly in the Dresden Collection formed by Augustus the Strong, and inventoried between 1721 and 1735.

## 17
## Charger

Kangxi, c.1710
Diameter : 18½ in (46.8 cm)

Decorated on the rim in underglaze blue diaper with six pictorial and twelve smaller panels in *famille verte*, and in the centre, encircled by *famille verte* flowers, a coat of arms beneath a coronet with the legend 'LUXENBURGH'.

It is not clear whether this series is earlier than the purely *famille verte* example (no. 16), or whether the two styles were sold as alternatives. The cities and states are the same.

It is probable that both series were imported over a number of years and were widely popular.

LITERATURE
Scheurleer, *Chinese Export Porcelain*, fig. 264, 'Groeningen' illustrated.

## 16
## Saucer Dish

Kangxi, c.1710
Diameter: 12¼ in (31.2 cm)

Moulded with everted and wavy rim, decorated in the *famille verte* palette with twelve petal-shaped panels alternately painted with antiques and figures within a diaper border. In the centre, encircled by flower sprays, a coat of arms with the legend 'ENGELANDT.'

This dish is from one of four series, examples of two being on this page, others shown being no. 24 and a Japanese version (no. 266). Each series probably comprised twenty-four armorials of Dutch cities and regions (including also France and England). There is little doubt that the V.O.C. ordered this porcelain.

The arms attributed to England mix fact with legend, for the Scottish quarter is shown as a thistle (the national flower) instead of a lion.

These pieces were intended for collection and display and not for use, although a number of barbers' bowls are recorded.

LITERATURE
Scheurleer, *Chinese Export Porcelain*, p. 128, 'Zutphen' illustrated in colour.
Howard, *Chinese Armorial Porcelain*, pp. 36–7, 'Luxenburgh'.
Howard & Ayers, *China for the West*, pp. 118–19, 'Holland' and 'Engelandt' illustrated.

## 18
## Plate

Kangxi, c.1715
Diameter: $8\frac{5}{8}$ in (22 cm)

Painted in *famille verte* translucent enamels with a yellow spotted deer looking up from beneath a pine tree at a heron in flight; six other herons on the rim.

There is a consistency about the painting of the many known examples of this design which suggests that they were painted over a short period.

It is unlikely that this was specially ordered in Europe, for all the elements of the design are Chinese. However, there are pieces with the Johanneum inventory mark – hence part of this 'service' (delivery) was in the collection of Augustus the Strong at Dresden after 1721.

LITERATURE
Jenyns, *Later Chinese Porcelain*, pl. xxx, 2.

## 19
## Octagonal Dish

Kangxi, c.1715
Length: $13\frac{3}{8}$ in (33.8 cm)

Of oblong shape with moulded and ridged rim, the ridge extending to the outer rim for a short section; decorated in *famille verte* with a heavily diapered well enclosing a kylin and two phoenixes. At the centre of the rim an armorial crest.

The crest could be of Wolff, Pemberton or Croachrod; the interest, however, lies in the carefully controlled manufacture of this service. The slightly enlarged flat area of the rim on this dish is matched in plates of the service by a space left clear in a diapered band for the crest.

A high degree of understanding was necessary between the private merchant who ordered the service and the Chinese merchant who took the order to Jingdezhen. This is lacking in some cases where, if the central picture is upright, the crest is not at the top.

LITERATURE
Howard, *Chinese Armorial Porcelain*, p. 189.

## 20
## Soup Plate

Kangxi, c.1718
Diameter: 8⅝ in (22 cm)

Of *famille verte*/Imari design with formal border and a central vase of flowers. The reverse of the rim also with floral scrollwork.

The border is of European leafy scrollwork in the manner of Jean Bérain, and is first noted on the armorial service made about 1712 for Dr Walker. In this example the work is looser and less well drawn. The centre is entirely of Chinese inspiration.

It seems likely that after the Walker and Somers armorial services which were specially designed, the Chinese adopted this effective border design for a short period for export use.

LITERATURE
Howard, *Chinese Armorial Porcelain*, p. 177, Walker and Somers services illustrated.

## 21
## Saucer Dish

Kangxi, c.1718
Diameter: 7¾ in (19.6 cm)

In Chinese Imari palette and decorated on the rim with antiques; inside a *rouge-de-fer* and gold scrollwork band, an armorial beneath a royal crown.

The service, which is a very large and elaborate one, has the arms of King Louis XV of France encircled by the Order of St Esprit (there is a similar service of this style with the arms of Philippe d'Orléans, the Regent).

Louis XV succeeded his great-grandfather Louis XIV in 1715 and died in 1774, and for the first eight years of his reign Philippe d'Orléans, his grandfather's first cousin, was Regent.

This service was much copied by Samson of Paris in the late 19th century.

LITERATURE
Beurdeley, *Porcelain of the East India Companies*, p.105, where the arms of the Regent, Philippe d'Orléans are illustrated.

## 23
## Dish

Kangxi, c.1720
Diameter: 16 in (40.6 cm)

Painted within a shaped octagonal panel, in *famille verte* enamels, with two lovers in a garden watched discreetly by a servant. The rim and well decorated in powder blue with floral gilding and eight small *famille verte* shaped reserves.

A number of vases and dishes for display were painted in this palette from about 1715 to 1725. The 'powder blue' effect was achieved by blowing powdered cobalt onto the biscuit surface before glazing. The reserves were masked and remained white. This is different from washes of underglaze blue which were used both before and after this time.

All examples of this ware with pictorial reserves are combined with *famille verte* enamels, which were rapidly displaced after 1722. The process must have been expensive and there are comparatively few pieces surviving.

## 22
## Charger

Kangxi, c.1720
Diameter: $17\frac{1}{2}$ in (44.3 cm)

Decorated in a rich mixture of palettes, with *rouge-de-fer* border and Chinese Imari flowers and leafy branches incorporating *famille verte* enamels. The arms are surprisingly not central and it is clear that they were drawn last.

Perhaps the richest armorial service of this time, it has the arms of the remarkable Craggs family. The Rt Hon. James Craggs was Postmaster-General in the reign of William and Mary (then a most lucrative post) but was heavily involved in the South Sea Company, and died in March 1721.

His son, James, was very widely travelled, and after being Ambassador to Spain became Secretary of State for War, but was taken ill with smallpox in the House of Commons and died, unmarried, a month before his father. The service could have been ordered by either.

LITERATURE
Tudor-Craig, *Armorial Porcelain of the 18th Century*, pp. 44–6 with portrait.
Le Corbeiller, *China Trade Porcelain*, pp. 44–5, covered bowl.
Howard, *Chinese Armorial Porcelain*, pp. 183–4.

## 24
## Charger

Kangxi, c.1720
Diameter: 18¾ in (47.6 cm)

Decorated on the rim with numerous shaped panels in 'rose Imari' (Imari palette with pink enamels added); the centre with the arms of Amsterdam, enclosed by columns and pediments in *famille verte*, and ladies in *famille rose*.

A very early example of the use of *famille rose* enamels on a dish essentially of underglaze blue, Imari and *famille verte* decoration, clearly intended as an addition to the long popular earlier series (see Nos 16, 17). Although this set may have included the same number of armorials, only about half are recorded.

LITERATURE
Scheurleer, *Chinese Export Porcelain*, fig. 265, 'Holland'.
Howard, *Chinese Armorial Porcelain*, pp. 36–7, 'Overysel'.

## 25

## Two Plates

Kangxi, c.1720
Diameter: 6¼ in (15.9 cm)

Decorated on the rim with blue and green leaves (part of the set of six in the collection), each having a figure from the Commedia dell'Arte and an inscription. Of the three series known, this is the most usually found.

The theatrical entertainment of the 'Italian Comedy' was at the height of its popularity when the financial scandals of 1718 to 1722 rocked the stability of Britain, France and Holland.

In England the 'South Sea Bubble', in France the upheaval brought about by Law's Louisiana,

Mississippi and Eastern Companies, and in Holland the fear that Dutch speculators would destroy the wealth of Holland, was countered by the V.O.C. with its own propaganda using scenes from the Italian comedy and a series of slogans: Here we see: '*De Actiemar op de tong*' – the march of the share values played on the tuning fork; '*Wie op Uÿtrech of Nieuw Amsterdam*' – who wants to speculate on Utrecht or New Amsterdam.

LITERATURE
Le Corbeiller, *China Trade Porcelain*, p. 43, illustrating one of a different series and one of Delft.
Howard & Ayers, *China for the West*, p. 234, where this whole set is illustrated and explained.

## 26
### Plate

Kangxi, c.1722
Diameter: 9 in (23 cm)

One of two services with the same arms and very similar design. This in underglaze blue, and in the centre a coat of arms in enamels.

In the 1720s and '30s it was not uncommon to order two armorial services with the same arms at the same time – one in underglaze blue and one in polychrome (usually *rouge-de-fer* and gold). The purpose is not clear – perhaps one for the country estate and one for London, or perhaps as 'best' and 'everyday'.

The arms are of Fortescue and Dormer, and the service was made for John Fortescue-Acland of Essex, Chief Justice of the Common Pleas in Ireland, who married as his second wife in 1721 Elizabeth, daughter of Sir Robert Dormer. He died in 1746 having been created Lord Fortescue of Credan, Co. Waterford.

LITERATURE
Howard, *Chinese Armorial Porcelain*, p. 168.

## 27
### Plate

Kangxi, c.1722
Diameter: 9 in (23 cm)

The second of the two services of this design made with these arms. The well and rim with *rouge-de-fer* and gold decoration and with three sprays of *famille verte* flowers. Perhaps the 'best' service made for John Fortescue-Acland – see above (no. 26).

LITERATURE
Howard, *Chinese Armorial Porcelain*, p. 198.

## 29
## Octagonal Dish

Kangxi, c.1722
Diameter: 12 in (30.4 cm)

With straight moulded edge and *famille verte* sprays enclosing a *rouge-de-fer* and gold well; with a central armorial beneath heavy mantling in *famille rose* enamels.

This is one of the earliest examples of *famille rose*, made for the very wealthy London merchant Sir John Lambert who, as a director of the South Sea Company, saw its failure and his own ruin in 1720/1 and died in 1723.

The service would have been ordered before the extent of his failure was known, and is one of two examples of armorial porcelain with *famille rose* which can be dated to 1721/2 (the other being the Visconti service).

LITERATURE
Howard, *Chinese Armorial Porcelain*, p. 206, an unusual tazza illustrated. Howard & Ayers, *China for the West*, p. 407; p. 452, a plate of the Visconti service.

## 28
## Plate

Kangxi, c.1722
Diameter: 9 in (23 cm)

With a large armorial in the centre within a well diaper of *rouge-de-fer* and gold; the rim with underglaze blue dragons, and an outer narrow band of *rouge-de-fer* and gold trellis.

This is one of no more than ten armorial services, apparently all for English families, painted with underglaze blue dragons on the rim. The arms are of William Heathcote, a Member of Parliament who was created a baronet in 1733. He married in 1720 the daughter of Thomas Parker, the Earl of Macclesfield, and Lord High Chancellor. A marriage was frequently the occasion for a dinner service to be ordered.

LITERATURE
Howard, *Chinese Armorial Porcelain*, p. 217.

## 30
## Plate

Yongzheng, c.1723
Diameter: 8½ in (21.6 cm)

In an unusual mixed palette combining an early *famille rose* central scene of an elderly man holding a parasol for a lady, and an Imari rim with blue trellis and four reserves.

This was painted very shortly after the introduction of the new opaque enamels on porcelain, of which the best known was a rich pink (Jacquemart & Le Blant writing in French in 1861 christened the opaque enamels *famille rose* – 'the rose family'). These colours had been introduced to China on enamelled ware about a decade earlier by Jesuit enamellers who had experience at Limoges.

Until that time underglaze blue, Imari and *famille verte* (Jacquemart & Le Blant so christened the translucent enamels) were almost the only palettes of export porcelain known in Europe. The period in which *famille verte* and *famille rose* overlapped was probably less than a decade.

LITERATURE
Jacquemart & Le Blant, *Histoire de la Porcelaine*, p. 67 where the term *famille verte* is first introduced; p. 77 where the term *famille rose* is first introduced.

## 32
### Plate

Yongzheng, c.1725
Diameter: $8\frac{7}{8}$ in (22.6 cm)

Decorated after a Japanese Imari original, the rim with three *famille verte* panels within underglaze blue scrollwork with flowers in red and gold. The central panel also in *famille verte* with trees and flowers (see no. 14).

A number of similar designs were produced based on Japanese patterns, some with more formal central panels with vases of flowers. A similar design was also copied in Europe in faience.

LITERATURE
Bondy, *K'ang Hsi*, pl. 157 for a similar design in the Dresden Collection.
Ayers, Impey & Mallet, *Porcelain for Palaces*, pp. 236, 253 (where a Warsaw version c.1776 is illustrated).

## 31
### Dish

Yongzheng, c.1723
Diameter: $13\frac{3}{4}$ in (34.9 cm)

Of hexagonal shape and decorated boldly with two bands of diaper in *rouge-de-fer* and gold enclosing an armorial beneath a baron's coronet. *Famille rose* shading on the motto scroll.

Charles Townshend, the son of Viscount Townshend (best known as 'Turnip Townshend' after he insisted on rotating his crops and planting the unfashionable turnip on his estates) was created a baron in his own right, as Lord Lynn, in May 1723 and in the same month married Audrey, the only daughter of Edward Harrison of Balls Park and formerly Governor of Madras.

Edward Harrison was already a prolific owner of Chinese armorial porcelain and had four services, but he was outdone by his son-in-law who had six (four with hexagonal dishes) – all within a decade.

LITERATURE
Howard, *Chinese Armorial Porcelain*, p. 220 where a milk jug of this service is illustrated with a piece from his father's service.

## 33
## Dish

Yongzheng, c.1726
Diameter: 12¾ in (32.5 cm)

With rim cut to make an embowed hexagonal shape (which may have been accidental, for another dish with straight edges is in this collection) and decorated in underglaze blue with central flower sprays and on the rim an armorial in the same style as the service shown opposite (no. 31).

The arms are also for Lord Lynn who married Audrey Harrison in 1723 and this service was probably ordered on a later voyage to China. The use of paler underglaze blue in the later 1720s is a noticeable feature of armorial porcelain services dateable to between 1725 and 1730.

LITERATURE
Howard, *Chinese Armorial Porcelain*, p.169.

## 34
## Plate

Porcelain Kangxi, c.1720; painting, c.1725
Diameter: 8¼ in (21 cm)

Circular, and of a size almost certainly made about 1720–25 (most Export plates were not made 9 in (23.8 cm) until about 1730). The painting, of two exotic birds with cherries, finely done in Holland.

It was natural that with the success of Chinese ware in Europe and the expansion of painting on porcelain at European factories, some Chinese porcelain should be painted in Europe, for it was cheaper to import it. Various European-inspired parrot and cherry designs were later copied again in China.

LITERATURE
Ayers, Impey & Mallet, *Porcelain for Palaces*, pp. 242, 243 (where Meissen porcelain is shown painted in Holland about the same time in similar colours).

## 35
## Plate

Yongzheng, c.1730
Diameter: 8⅜ in (21.4 cm)

One of very few designs with Export scenes in *rose-verte* enamels, embracing the change from the translucent *verte* enamels of the first quarter of the 18th century to the opaque *rose* enamels of the later quarters. A scarcely European ship lies at anchor by a rose-pink shoreline beneath the clouds, with a chop boat ferrying in between.

A considerable number of plates as well as tea services were made. Although there is a suggestion of European perspective, the design must have suggested the 'mysterious East' in the markets of Amsterdam.

LITERATURE
Howard & Ayers, *China for the West*, p. 218 where a teapot is also illustrated.

## 36
## Saucer Dish

Yongzheng, c.1730

Diameter: $8\frac{3}{8}$ in (21.5 cm)

Contrasting with its eastern counterpart above, this dish is of Chinese porcelain painted in Holland with European perspective, with a ship on the open seas and two others on the horizon. The narrow floral rim in pink and black copies the Chinese.

The realism of the rigging betrays a western hand. The design was a popular one which lasted more than a decade and some have the date 1700 on the stern of the ship and the arms of Zeeland below (sometimes with a *famille verte* border).

Every known example of this scene is a saucer dish and perhaps too many white saucer dishes had been imported, but this decoration turned a commercial failure into a success.

LITERATURE
Beurdeley, *Porcelain of the East India Company* (with 1700 date), cat. 244.

## 37
## Dish

Yongzheng, c.1730
Diameter: $12\frac{1}{2}$ in (31.8 cm)

Painted in shades of red-brown, black and gold, and traces of green within an underglaze blue border, with a European man and woman and their dog beneath a spreading tree beside a balustrade.

Although identifications of the European gentleman have included King Louis of France and, more plausibly, 'Governor Duff' (the Dutch Governor-General Duiven who served in that post in Batavia, 1729–31), there is no evidence that he is either, and a wealthy Dutch Friesian merchant and his wife are likely.

The scene was a popular one and there are other versions with the underglaze blue rim replaced by the same palette as that of the centre, and the scene even appears on Chinese lacquer of a slightly later period.

LITERATURE
Scheurleer, *Chinese Export Porcelain*, fig. 203 (where there is no underglaze blue).
Hervouët & Bruneau, *La Porcelaine des Companies des Indes à décor Occidental*, pp. 152–3 where both types of porcelain and a lacquer commode are illustrated.

## 38
## Saucer Dish

Yongzheng, c.1730
Diameter: 14 in (35.7 cm)

Decorated in *rose-verte* enamels with brilliant splashes of yellow, portraying a romantic scene of a seated lady waiting on a terrace with her maid while her lover scales the garden wall.

This is perhaps the earliest version of a scene which probably illustrates an elopement, for the lady waits with packed carriers.

Later versions of the scene, depicted sometimes within scrollwork and sometimes with other borders, continued for more than a decade, and indicate the popularity of the design, which was as romantic in the West as it was in the East. Such porcelain was undoubtedly ordered by various private merchants.

A particular feature of a number of scenes at this date was the painting of the willow tree – see also nos 39–41. It is of interest that the armorial service made for Lord King (see chapter 3), known to have been shipped in 1727, had the same willow on the rim, as did five other armorial services known from that time.

## 39
## Plate

Yongzheng, c.1730
Diameter: 8¾ in (22.3 cm)

Brightly enamelled in *rose-verte* enamels, incorporating a number of features of *famille verte* (the border and tree) and others of *famille rose*. The central scene with two horses gambolling.

In the ten years after the introduction of *famille rose*, the painting sometimes included both *famille verte* (translucent) and *famille rose* (opaque) enamels. It was a short-lived style, coinciding broadly with the Yongzheng period (1723–35).

Such pieces were probably chosen by merchants in Canton and the rim decoration of this plate is similar to that on a number of armorial services.

40
Plate

Yongzheng, c.1730
Diameter: 9 in (23 cm)

Decorated in *famille rose* enamels including yellow, the scene runs to the border and is entirely without European influence.

Depicting Chinese life, this design shows an official on his horse fording a river while his heavily laden servant wades behind him. The enamels are particularly rich.

It is a matter of conjecture how such porcelain was chosen and probably the merchants selected

small consignments from series shown to them in Canton. This plate, unlike others painted in the second half of the century, would have been decorated at Jingdezhen. The design would have appealed as illustrating a Chinese official travelling on business.

## 41
## Dish

Yongzheng, c.1730
Diameter: 22 in (55.8 cm)

Massively potted and decorated in the *rose-verte* palette with a peaceful lakeside scene, with groups of fishermen and their families picnicking on the banks. The border has an intricate yellow and green design.

This dish is most unusual in its size and choice of subject. Although the border suggests Export porcelain, the scene is entirely domestic Chinese and such porcelain must have been offered for sale to European merchants in shops in Canton. Undoubtedly it was for display rather than use.

Yellow enamel was at its most popular from 1730 to 1735, and this is confirmed by its use on a number of armorial services of that date.

## 42
## Dish

Yongzheng, c.1730
Diameter: 15¾ in (40 cm)

Richly painted in *rose-verte* enamels, the centre with two mandarin ducks swimming among lotus enclosed by a yellow enamel spearhead line at the well; on the rim the eight Daoist Immortals in choppy coastal seas.

This design is known on plates and is entirely Chinese, although made for export, and was almost certainly available for European private merchants in Canton. It must have proved popular for there are many examples known.

It was not long, however, before most Export ware was either floral or used European designs in the centre, for with the end of the Yongzheng period, which coincided with the new designs from Europe, both by Pronk and, later, after engravings, the oriental flavour was gradually lost.

## 44
## Dish

Yongzheng, c.1730
Diameter: 11 in (28 cm)

Very richly decorated, with six reserves on the rim containing butterflies and flowers divided by alternating gold and grey honeycomb diaper, the centre with a large armorial, and motto '*Sis faelix bis*'.

The arms are of Bisse impaling Bill – one might guess it from the motto – and of this family in the early 18th century Philip Bisse was Bishop of Hereford and married to the daughter of the Duke of Leeds, while Stephen Bisse was a director of the East India Company from 1732 to 1741.

Indeed the pun in the motto is not the only play on words, for the entwined snakes on the crest are certainly saying *bss-s-s* to each other.

LITERATURE
Howard, *Chinese Armorial Porcelain*, p. 234.

## 43
## Plate

Yongzheng, c.1730
Diameter: $8\frac{7}{8}$ in (22.8 cm)

Decorated brightly in rich enamels with three merchantmen, flying Dutch flags, sailing above an inscription '*Glucklig arivement*' ('Happy Homecoming'). The gilt trellis border and green diapered well enclose four flower sprays.

No engraving has been suggested for this scene and it is much more likely to copy an amateur painting. Few examples are known and there was probably only one small consignment of plates, undoubtedly ordered specially. The central ship has a name, possibly *St Vevuil*, and this may offer a clue to the exact date.

LITERATURE
Howard & Ayers, *China for the West*, p. 198.

## 45
## Soup Plate

Yongzheng, 1731
Diameter: 8½ in (21.7 cm)

Painted solely in underglaze blue, with an exotic bird on rockwork beneath trees; on the rim a simple crest.

This is an important service in terms of ceramic history, for it was one of two invoiced in 1731, both made for the Peers family of Chiselhampton Lodge in Oxfordshire (see chapters 2 and 4).

This service came via Madras with an invoice dated 19 November 1731 in Canton, while a *famille rose* service sailed direct from Canton to London on 8 January 1732. The *famille rose* service cost £76 for 450 pieces, and the blue and white one £13 for about 250 pieces.

LITERATURE
Tudor-Craig, *Armorial Porcelain of the 18th Century*, pp. 120, 121 (where plates of both services are illustrated with the invoice for the *famille rose* service).
Howard, *Chinese Armorial Porcelain*, p. 174 (blue and white plate), p. 249 (*famille rose* plate).
Le Corbeiller, *China Trade Porcelain*, pp. 52, 53 (where the blue plate and invoice for that service are illustrated).

## 46
## Soup Plate

Yongzheng, c.1733
Diameter: 9 in (23 cm)

Of unique design, the rim painted *en grisaille* with four broad panels of river scenery; in the centre a coat of arms.

The riverscapes, in the fine grey enamel only recently developed, are of London (across London Bridge), and the river below Canton. In the centre are the arms of Lee of Coton, and the service was ordered by Eldred Lancelot Lee (who died 1734) or his son.

As with the Valckenier services painted about five years later (see nos 61, 62), there is also a service with identical armorials, but omitting the riverscape scenes.

LITERATURE
Howard, *Chinese Armorial Porcelain*, p. 227.
Godden, *Oriental Export Market Porcelain*, frontispiece.

## 47
## Deep Plate

Yongzheng, c.1733
Diameter: 8½ in (21.6 cm)

Of eggshell porcelain and delicately painted in *famille rose* enamels, the centre with two Chinese shepherdesses and goats on a hillside. The gently flared rim with reserves of lotus, daisy and camellia on a pink cell diaper.

Although of a shape usually called a soup plate, there was no intention that such finely potted ware should be used for soup – rather for display. This is typical of the finer porcelain from Jingdezhen which supercargoes could buy specially from Chinese shops in Canton.

## 48
## Deep Plate

Yongzheng, c.1735
Diameter: 8⅞ in (22.6 cm)

A deep plate, decorated on the rim and well with honeycomb diaper and three panels of flowers. In the centre an unusual scene set in a hilly landscape with a Chinese girl seated on a white bull (with nose ring) while two attendants proffer flowers.

The meaning of this purely decorative plate is open to speculation, but is sufficiently similar to the wholly European fable of Europa and the Bull to admit comparison. There is no legend of a Chinese lady riding away on a white bull, and it is possible that it was an early suggestion of a supercargo to a Chinese merchant to have this scene painted in Chinese taste.

## 49
## Plate

Yongzheng, c.1735
Diameter: 9 in (23 cm)

Painted more delicately than the rich *famille rose* plate shown opposite (no. 51) with fishermen working in an estuary, but without any European influence, the Chinese scene running to the border.

This illustrates Chinese life in a way that would have been familiar to merchants residing part of the year in Canton and Macao. The fishermen use nets and stakes in a manner still followed today, and the Chinese houses by the shore are still a familiar sight to travellers.

This may have been another of the designs from which merchants chose. Certainly the comparative scarcity of such pieces does not indicate large consignments in the period immediately before the Dutch initiative with Cornelis Pronk (see nos 53–57).

## 50
## Enamel Plate

Yongzheng, c.1735
Diameter: 8¾ in (22.3 cm)

Decorated on white enamelled copper with a finely painted scene of a European lady and gentleman apparently engaged in a picnic. The wide border with lavender honeycomb diaper, on which are four groups of oriental fruit and insects. The well finely painted with yellow diaper and four rose-pink scrollwork reserves.

Where Europeans are finely painted during the Kangxi and Yongzheng periods, it is always possible that such scenes were made as much for the educated Chinese as for export. They display idealized scenes of Western life in the same way that idealized scenes of Chinese life were popular in Europe.

Such a piece would have been bought by a private trader as a speculative purchase from a Chinese merchant in Canton.

## 51
## Plate

Yongzheng, c.1735
Diameter: 8¼ in (21 cm)

Richly enamelled with a European lady and seated gentleman on a terrace watching a cockerel and a dog. The border in rose-pink with honeycomb diaper and four reserves with flowerheads between formal scrollwork.

As on the enamel plate (no. 50), this scene intends to illustrate a European domestic scene and may well be as much for Chinese eyes as for export. There are a number of versions, some without the lady and with other animals, sometimes coupling.

Such plates are more likely to have been purchased in china shops in Canton than ordered in quantity. The design was clearly popular judging from the number and variations still known, although this scene probably only appears on plates.

## 52
## Plate

Yongzheng, c.1735
Diameter: $8\frac{7}{8}$ in (22.6 cm)

Painted delicately on a central shaped panel with a lady seated before a cabinet on a garden terrace playing a *chin*, surrounded by a trellis diaper overlaid with red and gold scrollwork. The floral rim with four panels, alternating a cockerel and hen and two fish.

Before the development of European designs, the presentation of elegant Chinese interiors and domestic scenes, sometimes on eggshell porcelain plates, did much to stimulate the curiosity of European buyers. The quality of such painting was very high and this porcelain was selected by supercargoes in china shops in Canton.

# Cornelis Pronk (1691–1759)

In 1734 the Dutch East India Company (V.O.C.) appointed Cornelis Pronk to '. . . make all designs and models to our satisfaction, of all such porcelain as will be ordered from time to time in the Indies . . .'

Pronk had left the employ of the Company before the end of the decade and the number of designs known to be by him is small. Only four are now preserved in the Rijksmuseum, Amsterdam, recorded in the Company books as A, B, C and D (three of which are seen below). In a number of cases these were ordered in underglaze blue, *famille rose* and Chinese Imari and some versions were ordered from Japan. There are other designs, almost certainly by him, although no documentation survives for these.

By 1741 the Dutch supercargoes were reporting that, after visiting various China dealers, they had found the quotations too high and they were unlikely to order more. Nevertheless, they did order a number of further services, and it is clear that occasional further consignments were made, some as late as 1770.

LITERATURE
Jörg, *Pronk Porcelain* (essential reading on this subject).
Howard & Ayers, *China for the West*, pp. 292–305. (On page 294 a total of nine designs on porcelain are suggested.)

## 53
## Plate

Qianlong, c.1736-40
Diameter: 9 in (23 cm)

Painted in underglaze blue after an original drawing by Cornelis Pronk. Although clearly intended to have an oriental flavour, the design is western in execution.

The honeycomb border, interspersed with alternate cartouches of ladies and ducks, surrounds a central scene of a servant holding a parasol over her 'Chinese' mistress who is feeding three birds – two of a European species (a ruff and a spoonbill) – before European bullrushes.

This was the first of Pronk's four known designs – 'The lady with the parasol' ('A') – sent to China in 1734. It was ordered also in Imari and *famille rose* and there is a Japanese version. Although it was designed for the Company, within a short time Dutch supercargoes reported that the Chinese had copied the pattern and it was available for private traders in Canton.

LITERATURE
Jörg, *Pronk Porcelain*, pp. 14–17.
Lunsingh Scheurleer, *Chinese Export Porcelain*, pl. 194, coffee pot in the Rijksmuseum.
Howard & Ayers, *China for the West*, p. 298, cup and saucer.

**54**

**Plate**

Qianlong, c.1736–40

Diameter: $10\frac{1}{8}$ in (25.8 cm)

Painted in pastel shades, this scene and its border is the most artistic by Cornelis Pronk and it is known as 'The Four Doctors' or 'The Doctor's Visit to the Emperor' ('B').

Dr Jörg regards this design as the second produced by Pronk in 1735,

although a later version omitting the standing figure was sent to China in 1739. Already the intricate designs were causing production problems, for the volume of this new design was not to be great.

Jörg gives details of the Company shipments of this design up to 1739 in the three colours ordered, and after 1739 with figures shown in parentheses (actual deliveries may have differed).

LITERATURE
Jörg, *Pronk Porcelain*, pp. 26–30.
Lunsingh Scheurleer, *Chinese Export Porcelain*, pl. 198 (showing drawing with four figures).
Le Corbeiller, *China Trade Porcelain*, p. 56 (with drawing).

**55**

**Plate**

Qianlong, c.1738–40

Diameter: $10\frac{1}{4}$ in (26 cm)

Painted in enamels of which the dominant one is a rich turquoise green, this design is European in concept although oriental in intention. It is perhaps the most intricate of Pronk designs, and is known as 'The Arbour' ('D').

Dr Jörg records that this design is the fourth and last certain drawing by Cornelis Pronk for the Dutch

|  | Blue and white | Rose enamel | Chinese Imari |
|---|---|---|---|
| Dinner services of 371 pieces | 7 (60) | 6 (15) | 2 |
| Dinner services of 94 pieces | – (30) | – | – |
| Tea services | 5 (unrecorded) | 5 (unrecorded) | |
| Garnitures | 18* | 18 | 18 |
| Vases and basins (two sizes) | 5 | – | 5 |

* See one illustrated in this book, no. 284.

East India Company in 1737.
Quoting from a letter from the
supercargoes, Jörg says that the
earlier designs are reported to have
'proved quite expensive and for this
reason they did not dare to have the
whole quantity made.'

This was one of the last efforts to
prepare completely European
designs (the ground of 'mosaic'
having proved particularly time-
consuming) and a new idea of
placing European engravings within
standard borders was shortly to
prove more successful.

LITERATURE
Jörg, *Pronk Porcelain*, pp. 34–35.
Le Corbeiller, *China Trade Porcelain*,
p. 59.
Howard & Ayers, *China for the
West*, p. 301.

## 56
## Plate

Qianlong c.1738–40
Diameter: 9 in (23 cm)

Painted in underglaze blue with
exactly the same scene as above.

Of the first Pronk design there are
plates in four versions: Chinese
Imari, *famille rose*, underglaze blue
and Japanese Imari. The second
design 'B' had two versions and was
ordered in three colours. Within
three years it was realized that the
costs of these special designs were so
much greater than for standard
Chinese patterns that both
variations and quantities had to be
reduced. These are the only two
colourings of design 'D'.

## 57
## Plate

Japanese, c.1738
Diameter: 10½ in (26.6 cm)

Decorated at Arita in Japan in imitation of *famille rose* after Pronk's first design (no. 53).

Jörg mentions that the V.O.C. abandoned its efforts to have this design painted in Japan in 1740 because of price (porcelain painters were known to be paid more in Japan than in China).

The few pieces that do exist were clearly samples or made in small batches in underglaze blue and polychrome to test costs.

LITERATURE
Jörg, *Pronk Porcelain*, p. 73 where examples of both Japanese versions are illustrated.

## 58
## Plate

Yongzheng, c.1735
Diameter: 9 in (23 cm)

Simply decorated with a large 'butterfly', probably an Atlas moth. The rim with two fine lines in gold.

The Chinese word for butterfly *tie* signifies 'long life' through a punning association, and such a plate would express this wish to the owner.

Such porcelain would have been obtainable from merchants in Canton, for it is unlikely that any special order would have been made by a European.

LITERATURE
Howard & Ayers, *China for the West*, p. 149 for a similar plate.

## 59
## Plate

Yongzheng, c.1735
Diameter: 9 in (23 cm)

The centre with four butterfly wings enclosing a bee. On a rich rose-enamelled and trellised rim, four cartouches – two with armorials and two with a cypher beneath a coronet.

The arms are of Grimaldi and a branch of this family, originally of Genoa, acquired the Seigneurie of Monaco in 1331. The cypher is not clear, but in 1731 James I, who succeeded his wife Princess Louise Hyppolite (who survived the death of her father Prince Antoine I in 1731 for less than a year), ruled for a short period before 'withdrawing to the comforts of Paris' in 1733, leaving the Principality to their thirteen-year-old son, Honoré III. Prince Honoré reigned for sixty years until the Principality was merged for a period with the Département of Alpes Maritimes in 1793.

It seems possible that the butterflies and bee were intended to wish long life and industry to the young prince.

## 60
## Plate

Yongzheng, c.1735
Diameter: 10½ in (26.7 cm)

Painted to special order during the same period as pieces designed by Cornelis Pronk. Almost certainly for the Dutch market, with a spray of exotic flowers with caterpillar and butterfly within a gilt band of underglaze blue and an elaborate European scrollwork border.

This design, which is also known entirely in underglaze blue, is copied from a painting by the Dutch botanist Maria Sybille Merian (1646–1717), who travelled extensively in the Dutch West Indies. There are garniture designs attributed to Pronk with similar flowers and butterflies.

LITERATURE
Jacquemart & Le Blant, *Histoire de la Porcelaine*, pl. XI.
Howard & Ayers, *China for the West*, pp. 304–5 (also illustrating a vase of very similar design).

## 61
## Plate

Qianlong, c.1738
Diameter: 9 in (23 cm)

Finely decorated on the rim and in the well with floral gilding picked out with some blue enamel and punctuated by four lobed cartouches, three of which have scenes *en grisaille*, and the fourth, the crest repeated. In the centre the full arms of Valckenier of Amsterdam.

This is a remarkable service and one of four with these arms (there being another below; a blue and white dinner service of possibly a little later than this one; and a set of 17th-century Japanese jugs in underglaze blue).

The only scene identified with certainty is the King William Gate at Cleves to the left of the arms, although that on the right may be a Dutch East India Company warehouse.

The service was probably made for Adriaan Valckenier (1695–1751), who served in Batavia from 1715 to 1741, where he was latterly Governor-General, but left after the Massacre of the Chinese in the previous year, for which he was held in part responsible.

LITERATURE
Le Corbeiller, *China Trade Porcelain*, pp. 86–8, gives extended details and an illustration of the Cleves engraving.
Ayers, Impey & Mallet, *Porcelain for Palaces*, p. 98 where a Japanese jug is illustrated.

## 62

## Plate

Qianlong, c.1738
Diameter: $8\frac{3}{4}$ in (22.4 cm)

Decorated on the rim with three extended gilt floral sprays and in the centre with the full arms of Valckenier of Amsterdam.

This service is a simplified version of no. 61 and may have been ordered at the same time, or on the next voyage (see also a jug of this service, no. 247).

As with the Lee of Coton service (no. 46), it seems probable that most of the service did not have the special rim design but that a smaller set of plates did (see no. 61). These may, however, be part of a separate service.

LITERATURE
Le Corbeiller, *China Trade Porcelain*, p. 87.

the normal price for armorial porcelain. The quality and intricacy of painting was not excelled in the 18th century.

LITERATURE
Tudor-Craig, *Armorial Porcelain of the 18th Century*, p. 121.
Howard, *Chinese Armorial Porcelain*, frontispiece, p. 398.
Howard & Ayers, *China for the West*, pp. 413–15, the original painting illustrated.
Christie's 3 March 1975, 100 pieces sold (for 58,000 guineas).

## 63
## Plate

Qianlong, c.1740 or 1743
Diameter: 9 in (23 cm)

Enamelled without a trace of Chinese influence in rich *famille rose* enamels, after a European painted pattern still possessed by the family, on the reverse of which is written 'The Arms of Leake Okeover Esqre. of Okeover near Ashbourn in the Peak in the County of Derbyshire – a pattern for China plate. Pattern to be returned.' (It is said that this original was painted by Arthur Devis Sr, 1711–87).

Two deliveries of this porcelain were made – in 1740 and 1743, the first invoice listing 100 pieces for £99 11s 10d, and the second being from the Jerusalem Coffee House in Change Alley. The price of about £1 per piece was about ten times

## 64
## Saucer Dish

Qianlong, c.1740
Diameter: 7¾ in (19.8 cm)

Decorated in the centre with exotic Chinese flowers within a rim design of six shaped oval floral panels edged with gold scrollwork between wedges of Chinese decoration.

This apparently Chinese design clearly derives from the second design of Cornelis Pronk (see no. 54), 'The Four Doctors', which has a very similar border formation but with more elaborate details.

It is probable that the interest caused in Canton by the Pronk border designs prompted a Chinese workshop to produce a similar effect at much lower cost, using patterns with which it was more familiar, for Dutch supercargoes or private traders of other countries.

## 65
## Plate

Qianlong, c.1740
Diameter: 9 in (23 cm)

Decorated with an idealized European harbour scene within a shaped cartouche set on a *bianco-sopra-bianco* ground; on the rim four sprays of flowers.

The scene is a finely drawn painting of merchants on an imaginary European coastline awaiting the arrival of a merchantman from the East. The style is in the manner of Meissen *Hausmaler* painting and while there would have been an original European design, it would probably have been on porcelain.

LITERATURE
Hervouët & Bruneau, *La Porcelaine des Compagnies des Indes à Décor Occidental*, p. 345 where an identical plate is illustrated.

## 67
## Plate

Qianlong, c.1740
Diameter: 8¾ in (22.3 cm)

Finely drawn and painted in unusual pastel shades with a gentleman fishing; the border with honeycomb diaper in grey and gold, punctuated with four mountain lake scenes.

This is one of the more popular designs of the 1740s and appears with at least three borders and in three different colourings, of which this is probably the earliest.

The use of a popular engraving 'Le Pêcheur', after the 16th-century Dutch artist Abraham Bloemaert, was assured of almost certain success on porcelain, as it was already a popular print. After the initial, possibly V.O.C., order, variations would have been available to private merchants in Canton, probably with less expensive borders.

LITERATURE
Beurdeley, *Porcelain of the East India Companies*, cat. 123 (with border as no. 68).
Lunsingh Scheurleer, *Chinese Export Porcelain*, pl. 206 (the plate *en grisaille* and an original engraving illustrated).
Howard & Ayers, *China for the West*, p. 369 (the plate *en camaïeu* and a simpler border).

## 66
## Plate

Qianlong c.1740
Width: 9 in (23 cm)

Decorated at the rim with fine gold scrollwork after Meissen porcelain of the previous decade, and in the centre *en grisaille* with a marriage beneath a classical dome and between garlanded pillars; in the foreground tritons and sea nymphs revel. Above the two outside pillars are coats of arms.

This is a plate from one of about ten services with the same scene but different armorials on the columns. All the identified arms are Dutch, but these are not known. In spite of its complexity, such a standard design would have helped to reduce the cost for what otherwise would have been a very expensive style, even though painted in one colour with gilding – it might also have enabled delivery to be made more quickly.

The design is only known in this form and was probably made for no more than two or three seasons. A plaque in the Victoria and Albert Museum with this scene is dated 1741.

LITERATURE
Howard & Ayers, *China for the West*, p. 394, a similar plate but with the arms of Geelvinck and Graafland.

## 68
## Plate

Qianlong, c.1740
Diameter: 9⅛ in (23.3 cm)

Depicting in sepia a countrywoman with a baby on her back, holding the palm of a man whose horse is held by a groom while his dogs sit in the foreground. The rim with an intricate European scrollwork border *en grisaille* in the manner of du Paquier.

This painting closely follows a contemporary engraving 'The Fortune Teller' by J. Smith. A Chinese reverse painting on glass of the late 18th century in a Spanish collection also has this scene, with the signature 'Smith'.

The use of a European engraving over a period of some fifty years in decorating porcelain and in glass painting illustrates the way in which Chinese workshops may have held designs for varied use over a considerable period. Another version of the scene with a different border (of cornucopiae) is known.

LITERATURE
Howard & Ayers, *China for the West*, pp. 372–3.

## 70
## Dish

Qianlong, c.1745
Diameter: 11¼ in (28.6 cm)

Of shaped rim with a rose border derived from the shell or cornucopia design of a few years earlier. In the centre an armorial within a display of flags.

The arms are of Pignatelli and the service was made for Prince Pignatelli of Naples, a close relative of Antonius Pignatelli, elected Pope Innocent XII in 1691.

## 69
## Plate

Qianlong, c.1740
Diameter: 9 in (23 cm)

Decorated in underglaze blue with a shell-and-cornucopia border and central scene. On the reverse the figure 15.

This is one of twenty-four plates (and dishes) with scenes of the cultivation and marketing of tea. Although there are occasional examples of the same scene with different numbers, no. 15 shows the tricky navigation of the bales of tea on rafts over the cataracts on the river down to Canton.

The border was probably first used (in *famille rose*) on an armorial service for the Snoek family of Amsterdam. It is possible that there is some link between the two

services, for a set of twenty-four of these plates is known in Holland.

The border and series of scenes were specially commissioned after a set of Chinese paintings of tea cultivation.

LITERATURE
Howard & Ayers, *China for the West*, pp. 214–15 (nos 11, 23); p. 396, Snoek armorial dish.
Other examples:
No. 12, Peabody Museum, Salem.
Nos 13, 21, Metropolitan Museum, New York.
A tureen, dish and sauceboat, Fries Museum, Leeuwarden.

## 71
## Plate

Qianlong, c.1740
Diameter: 9 in (23 cm)

Painted with a riverside scene within a narrow band of gilt scrollwork; the rim heavily decorated in *bianco-sopra-bianco*.

The scene is painted in the manner of the Meissen *Hausmaler* ('home painters'); for about two decades from 1740 Chinese porcelain was painted in this manner after samples taken to China, often with scenes within shaped cartouches intricately decorated with gold and enamel scrollwork. The volume of specially commissioned porcelain in the style of Meissen was, for a time, perhaps third only to painting after engravings and armorials.

In this example, the scene fills the whole centre of the plate and the central figure with a crown is traditionally (and probably correctly) identified as Peter the Great, Emperor of Russia, who arrived in Amsterdam in 1697 and worked incognito at the small Dutch port of Zaandam. There are at least four variants of this theme with a crowned workman among the clutter of riverside wharves.

LITERATURE
Hervouët & Bruneau, *La Porcelaine des Compagnies des Indes à Décor Occidental*, pp. 340–361, section illustrating some forty examples 'in the manner of Meissen'.

## 72
## Plate

Qianlong, c.1745
Diameter: 9 in (23 cm)

Decorated in the centre with a similar design to the Grimaldi service (no. 59). On the rim an armorial with a gilt trellis band enclosing three sprays of flowers.

The arms are of Hesketh and the service was probably ordered for Thomas Hesketh, who came of age in 1749, fourteen years after his father's death. The central design of butterflies and bee could again indicate industry and long life. He was created a baronet in 1761, and died at the age of fifty in 1778.

This service is of particular interest as it has a number of different central designs.

LITERATURE
Howard, *Chinese Armorial Porcelain*, p. 338 where a dish with a central pheasant is illustrated.

## 73
## Plate

Qianlong, c.1745
Width: 8¾ in (22.3 cm)

Decorated *en grisaille*, the rim with four shaped oval cartouches – two with landscapes and two with a bird on a branch; in the centre a doubtful young girl being caressed by an elderly man with broad-rimmed hat beneath a canopy, with a distant landscape to the right.

The print is not identified, but the type of hat may suggest a Jewish suitor and the subject may therefore be biblical. Certainly the well-drawn sandals must be copied from the original European engraving.

This example of a rare engraving being copied onto a Chinese plate was probably for a limited order with a specific market in mind –

THE DINNER SERVICE: PLATES AND DISHES

biblical or erotic. The use of
enamelling *en grisaille* would have
helped reduce the cost.

LITERATURE
Hervouët & Bruneau, *La Porcelaine
des Compagnies des Indes à Décor
Occidental*, p. 165. The same scene
but with different landscape and
earlier border.

## 74
## Plate

Qianlong, c.1745
Diameter: $8\frac{7}{8}$ in (22.8 cm)

Painted in underglaze blue with an
English mansion between trees in
parkland, within a delftware scroll
border and a Chinese design at the
well.

There is considerable similarity
between this house and that on an
English delftware plate, illustrated
in the catalogue of an exhibition at
the Rijksmuseum, which is certainly
Burghley House. Although there is
no other obvious candidate, it is
possible that the building on this
Chinese plate could be another
Elizabethan mansion.

Burghley House was, however,
painted very accurately *en grisaille*,
with armorials of about 1735, on a
fine bowl which is still at the house.

LITERATURE
Michael Archer, *Catalogue of an
Exhibition of English Delftware*,
no. 112.
Howard & Ayers, *China for the
West*, p. 261.

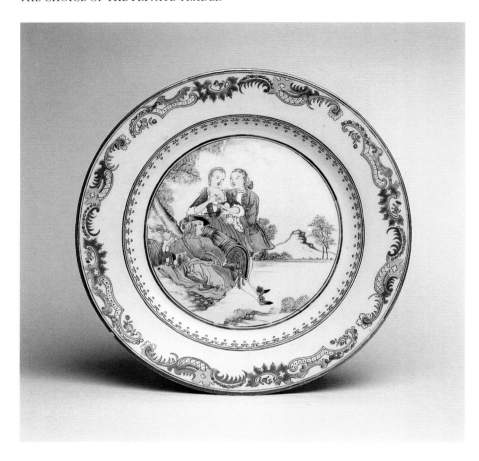

## 76
## Saucer Dish

Qianlong, c.1745
Diameter: 11 in (28.1 cm)

Precisely painted with flower and fruit sprays in unfamiliar tones of *famille rose* enamels; the rim with four cartouches – two with fish and two with eagles under 'petal coronets'.

The design betrays much that is European inspired but in spite of considerable speculation, it has not been possible to explain the fish and the eagles. There is a similar blue and white service and both have been ascribed to Madame de Pompadour on the grounds that her maiden name was Poisson and that the eagle was King Louis XV. This seems unlikely, although there is no other obvious interpretation.

There can be no doubt that this service was a private order of considerable importance, for it contained many rare or unique jars, vases, jugs, tureens and other pieces, but the original owner, though almost certainly French, remains obscure.

LITERATURE
Beurdeley, *Porcelain of the East India Companies*, cat. 190, pot-pourri. Howard & Ayers, *China for the West*, p. 443.

## 75
## Plate

Qianlong, c.1745
Width: 8¾ in (22.5 cm)

Decorated on the rim with feathery scrolls in bright enamels; the central scene after a European original of a troubadour with his lute beneath a tree, sitting beside two barrels with a decanter and wine glasses, while a young man caresses a girl beside him.

This version of a country music party has a distinctly Continental flavour and is one of at least six such scenes which illustrate musicians in gently amorous situations – all after European originals of the period 1735–50.

LITERATURE
Hervouët & Bruneau, *La Porcelaine des Compagnies des Indes à Décor Occidental*, pp. 184–8.

## 77
## Plate

Qianlong, c.1745
Diameter: 9 in (23 cm)

Painted with an imaginary scene of
a breadfruit tree with a floral
garland and a coconut palm to the
left. In the foreground an altar with
two hearts, two doves on Cupid's
quiver, a shepherd's pipes and two
recumbent hounds – the whole now
known as the 'Valentine Pattern'.

This scene is copied exactly from
the service made for Lord Anson in
1743 and was almost certainly based
on a drawing by Anson's official
artist, Piercy Brett, who sailed with
him on his voyage of circumnavigation. The idea was certainly
inspired by their stay on Tenian
Island to collect breadfruit trees for
the British West Indian colonies. An
illustration in *Anson's Voyages* shows
a very similar breadfruit tree and
palm, while other allusions are to
absent loved ones.

The armorial is of Stewart, Lord
Blantyre, made for Walter the 8th
Baron whose younger brother
Charles was in the East India
Company, and later on the
Supreme Council of Bengal (see
no. 121 for the sauce tureens from
services for his two brothers).

LITERATURE
Howard, *Chinese Armorial Porcelain*,
pp. 46–7, where Anson's service is
illustrated, together with the print
from Anson's *Voyages*.

## 79
## Plate

Qianlong, c.1750
Diameter: 9 in (23 cm)

More crudely decorated than
no. 78, with a simplified Valentine
pattern. The tree no longer
resembling a breadfruit tree at all,
the faithful hounds distorted; the
rim with a sketchy version of the
scroll-and-shell pattern popular
since 1745.

The Valentine pattern still had a
popularity which saw it produced in
underglaze blue with hounds and
puppies and with Chinese-looking
shepherds in European clothes
seated beneath pine trees. It was
copied at Worcester and elements
appear on Chinese snuffboxes and
rim cartouches for a decade after
Anson's service. It became, in fact,
part of the repertoire of Chinese
workshops in Canton.

## 78
## Plate

Qianlong, c.1748
Diameter: 9 in (23 cm)

Decorated with a simplified version
of the Valentine pattern (omitting
breadfruit, palm tree, altar and
birds). The rim with a European
scroll and an armorial.

The arms are of George
Cholmondeley, Viscount Malpas,
who married in January 1747

Hester, the daughter and heir of Sir
Francis Edwardes. The service is
unlikely to have arrived in England
until two years after the Blantyre
one and the degree of simplification
in so short a time shows how
quickly an original design was
adapted and simplified by Chinese
painters – sometimes to save
expense.

LITERATURE
Howard, *Chinese Armorial Porcelain*,
p. 331.

## 80
## Plate

Qianlong c.1750
Diameter: 9 in (23 cm)

Decorated with an elaborate
cartouche and two cyphers beneath
a coronet, within a band of floral
scrollwork at the rim and a gilt-
patterned well. About this are a
Chinese shepherdess and a seated
man with a book beneath a tree;
above are three angels appearing
from the clouds, and below a seated
dog beside a shepherd's crook.

This is undoubtedly a marriage
service, but it still contains a
number of elements of the
Valentine pattern. It is not clear if it
was designed specially in Europe by
someone who already knew the
earlier services inspired by that
made for Anson, or whether it was
adapted by an enterprising supercargo or Chinese artist in Canton.

## 82
## Plate

Qianlong, c.1750
Diameter: 9 in (23 cm)

Decorated with six women drawing water from a well and the figure of a man approaching, within a scroll-and-shell border – a design adapted from the border of silver salvers of that period.

The figures are biblical and represent Rebecca and her friends drawing water at the well as Abraham's servant approaches (Genesis xxiv).

The dating of this service is quite exact, for a plate with the same design and border was in the cargo of *Geldermalsen*, which sank in January 1752 between Canton and Batavia, salvaged by Captain Michael Hatcher.

LITERATURE
Hervouët & Bruneau, *La Porcelaine des Compagnies des Indes à Décor Occidental*, p. 259, with different border.
Howard & Ayers, *China for the West*, p. 308 where further biblical details are given.

## 81
## Plate

Qianlong, c.1750
Diameter: 9 in (23 cm)

Decorated with scroll-and-shell border in gold, and an elaborate central armorial surrounded by eight smaller named coats of arms.

This service is the ultimate illustration of a family tree on Chinese porcelain, with the quarterly arms of Theodorus van Reverhorst in the centre and the arms of eight named ancestors about it. On the left, his paternal great-grandparents and on the right, his maternal great-grandparents. (It was considered a matter of particular pride to be able to claim eight armigerous great-grandparents).

Theodorus van Reverhorst was a member of the Court of Justice in Batavia and retired to Holland in 1752.

LITERATURE
Lunsingh Scheurleer, *Chinese Export Porcelain*, cat. 148, 173, 274 for other pieces from this service.
Howard & Ayers, *China for the West*, pp. 400–1 for family tree and further historical details.

## 83
## Plate

Qianlong, c.1750
Diameter: 9 in (23 cm)

Decorated with a rural scene within a scroll-and-shell border in gold.

This scene is clearly based on a European engraving, and probably one of the many which presented an idealized view of rural toil in the 18th century. It is possible that it could have biblical connotations.

There is a later version of the same scene with the same border, made about 1800. The design is rare and possibly only a small consignment was ordered.

LITERATURE
Hervouët & Bruneau, *La Porcelaine des Compagnies des Indes à Décor Occidental*, p. 87, a version of c.1800.

## 84
## Dish

Qianlong, c.1750
Diameter: 14 in (35.6 cm)

Decorated with a border usually confined to armorial porcelain with four rim cartouches; in the centre, on a hatched grey background, the bust of a lady.

The rim panels are a simplified version of the design first painted on the service made for Admiral Anson in 1742/3, which illustrated more accurately Plymouth Sound and Whampoa in the Pearl River in two long panels. In 1745 the scenes became shorter and four in number, but by 1750 the ships sailing down Plymouth Sound had acquired Chinese mountains in the background, although the scene at Whampoa remained more accurate.

The bust in the central medallion is not identified, but is possibly after a coin or an engraving of a marble bust. Since all the known services with this border are for the English market, it seems likely that the portrayal is English – possibly Queen Caroline, wife of George II, who died in 1737 aged fifty-four, and whose portraits are not unlike this bust.

LITERATURE
Howard, *Chinese Armorial Porcelain*, pp. 46–7 where the rim panels are analysed.
Kerslake, *Early Georgian Portraits*, pl. 103, bust of Queen Caroline.

## 85
## Plate

Qianlong, c.1750
Diameter: 9 in (23 cm)

Painted with a country scene of a knight on horseback led by his servant, while two girls watch from below a tree; the rim with four landscape cartouches *en grisaille*.

This painting of Don Quixote with a barber's bowl on his head, led by his servant Sancho Panza, is a Chinese adaptation from an earlier service, itself a copy of the engraving by J. Folkema after a painting by C. Coypel.

The earlier Chinese plates were produced shortly after Folkema's engraving of 1741, while this version followed a popular edition of Don Quixote published in Dutch in 1746.

The descendants of a British East India captain, Philip Bromfield, had a dinner service of this pattern, which was sold in London in 1968.

LITERATURE
Williamson, *The Book of Famille Rose*, pl. XXIV, a teapot illustrated.
Lloyd Hyde, *Oriental Lowestoft*, p. 88, pl. XV, the earlier service.

## 86
## Plate

Qianlong, c.1750
Diameter: 11 in (28.1 cm)

Of octagonal shape with central coat of arms within an intricate polychrome diaper border.

This armorial service with the arms of Chase has always excited more than average interest, for it was once believed that the owner could have been Samuel Chase, a signer of the American Declaration of Independence. In fact it was made for Sir Richard Chase, Sheriff of Essex in 1744, who was a wealthy ironmonger of Gracechurch Street in London. (Le Corbeiller illustrated in *China Trade Porcelain* the bookplate of Samuel Chase, which was actually very similar to the arms of Towneley – his uncle's wife was a Miss Towneley – but a careful search by the Towneley family in England has not been able to identify her).

LITERATURE
Howard, *Chinese Armorial Porcelain*, p. 259.
Le Corbeiller, *China Trade Porcelain*, pp. 61–63.

## 87
## Dish

Qianlong, c.1750
Diameter: 12½ in (31.7 cm)

Of wavy edge, decorated in underglaze blue with traces of gilding washed off from long immersion. The floral border encloses a band of trellis and a river scene with pavilions.

Unlike the Hatcher salvage of a late Ming cargo (see no. 3), it proved possible to identify the wrecked ship as the Dutch East Indiaman *Geldermalsen*, which sank on 3 January 1752 with a well documented cargo of more than 220,000 pieces, of which about 172,000 were salvaged in good condition.

No study of Export porcelain in the middle of the 18th century would be complete without careful comparison with this cargo, which was auctioned in Amsterdam 234 years later under the name 'Nanking' (a name chosen purely for its marketing appeal). This design (known as 'Three Pavilions') was one of a considerable number of patterns named for the occasion and was not private cargo.

LITERATURE
Christie's Amsterdam, sale catalogue, 28 April–2 May 1986 (over 5,800 lots, this pattern Lots 3702–57 including nine services of up to 360 pieces each).
Jörg, *The Geldermalsen, History and Porcelain*, illustration of a service p. 60.
Hatcher & Thorncroft, *The Nanking Cargo*.
Sheaf & Kilburn, *The Hatcher Porcelain Cargoes*, p. 118, a well gilded example (in reverse); p. 133.

## 88
## Saucer Dish

Qianlong, c.1750
Diameter: 11½ in (29 cm)

Decorated in underglaze blue (without gilding) with a pavilion and garden with a lattice fence; the rim with three large sprays of flowers.

This was perhaps the most sought after pattern (called at auction 'Lattice Fence') from the *Geldermalsen* cargo (see no. 87). The design extended to every shape used in a dinner service including tureens, saucer dishes, salts (see no. 128) and covered jars with handles – possibly for mustard. A number of assembled services of this pattern, of which the largest was 380 pieces, were sold at auction in Amsterdam in 1986 in exactly the same way as in the 18th century.

(171 dinner services are recorded as being on the *Geldermalsen*, ordered by the V.O.C.)

LITERATURE

Christie's Amsterdam, sale catalogue, 28 April–2 May 1986: Lots 3501–97 being of this pattern and Lot 3532 being a 380-piece service sold for Dfl 770,000 (at the time £240,000 or $425,000). Jörg; Hatcher & Thorncroft; Sheaf & Kilburn, as no. 87.

# 89
# Plate

Qianlong, c.1750
Diameter: 9 in (23 cm)

Decorated in underglaze blue with three large sprays of flowers on the rim, a band of trellis, and central coat of arms.

It is of interest to compare this service, which was specially ordered, with two designs from the wreck of the *Geldermalsen* in 1752, one of which has three similar sprays of flowers and the other a similar trellis. Clearly the armorial was specially ordered, but the rest of the design was a standard one from the early 1750s.

The arms are of Sykes of Sledmere, after an original bookplate by William Stephens of Cambridge. This was made either for Richard Sykes (who had ordered an earlier service through the Swedish East India Company), or for his brother Mark, who was created a baronet in 1783. A blue and white service of over 700 pieces appears in the Sledmere inventory of 1755 and it seems likely that this piece is from it, although an armorial is not mentioned.

LITERATURE

Howard, *Chinese Armorial Porcelain*, p. 583–4

## 91
## Plate

Qianlong, c.1755
Diameter: $9\frac{1}{8}$ in (23.1 cm)

Of shaped rim and painted in puce enamel *en camaieu* with gilding at the well; the central scene after a European engraving.

The pride of the Dutch in their seaborne empire is epitomized by a number of prints illustrating Holland receiving tribute from the four continents (the earliest set being published in 1663). This plate illustrates Batavia (with the city in the background – the hub of her eastern possessions), with eastern merchants proffering gifts with royal regalia, watched by the Dutch lion and Mercury, the God of Commerce.

LITERATURE
Beurdeley, *Porcelain of the East India Companies*, cat. 176.
Howard & Ayers, *China for the West*, p. 200.

## 90
## Plate

Qianlong, c.1750
Diameter: 9 in (23 cm)

Of scalloped circular shape with elaborate European panelled border, with peacocks displayed and a stylized domestic garden scene in the centre below a cartouche with two cyphers separated by a heart pierced by arrows.

While it is tempting to label this as a marriage service, almost certainly for the Dutch market, the scene appears to illustrate a middle-aged couple with their children; their daughter behind her mother, and son shooting. This is more likely to be an anniversary service.

The design is perhaps unique and the original amateur drawing would have been given to the Chinese for copying within a border then popular. The somewhat naïve design and cyphers suggest a captain or supercargo painting it himself. The border, copying a Viennese du Paquier design, was popular for about two decades (see no. 68 of c.1740 and no. 210 of c.1760).

## 92
# Plate

Qianlong, c.1756
Diameter: 9 in (23 cm)

The centre painted with a ship under sail (although the gangplank is down and she was probably at anchor!). On the plain rim the inscription 'T: SCHN: VRYBURG CEVOERT DOOR; CAPITEYN JACOB RUZIK IN CHINA INT ITAAR 1756'.

The 'Portrait of the Ship Vryburg, Captain Jacob Ryzik in China in 1756' is clearly taken from a drawing on the spot to which the sails have been added. There are some variations of inscription known and examples are recorded with the ship facing in the opposite direction.

This was enamelled in Canton to the order of Captain Ryzik and other versions were made for the *Vryburg*'s officers.

The same ship, without the inscription, is also known on heavily potted dishes of the 19th century and the original pattern may well have been handed down as a sample for other ships on Chinese porcelain.

LITERATURE
Beurdeley, *Porcelain of the East India Companies*, pl. XII.
Lunsingh Scheurleer, *Chinese Export Porcelain*, cat. 244, p. 144 for other inscriptions.
Jörg, *The Dutch China Trade*, p. 147 (for C. Schooneman, first mate).

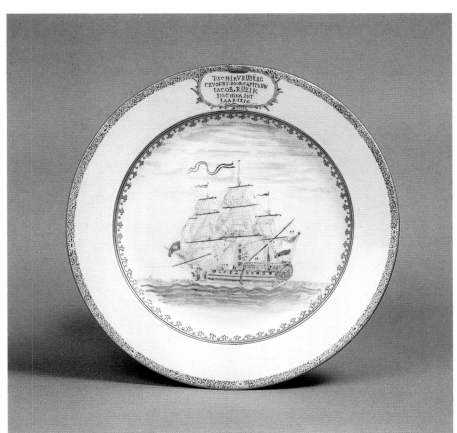

## 93
## Plate

Qianlong, c.1765
Diameter: 9 in (23 cm)

Painted across the centre with a harbour inn, vessels tied up and small boats, all within a border with eight small sprays of European flowers.

This is a view of the Stadts Herbergh on the waterfront at Amsterdam, built in 1662 (the porcelain coincides with the centenary of the building). The scene is well known but no exact original engraving has been found – perhaps the original of the porcelain was a specially prepared watercolour, for the result is well balanced.

It is clear that there was a considerable order, for a number of plates survive and there were also tea pieces. The border is standard; indicating that the whole design was not sent from Europe, only the central scene.

LITERATURE
Le Corbeiller, *China Trade Porcelain*, p. 108, illustrating a different engraving of the same building. Catalogue of the Reeves Collection, cat. 17 where a tea caddy is illustrated.

## 94
## Plate

Qianlong, c.1768
Diameter: 8½ in (21.7 cm)

Of octagonal shape with a central pictorial armorial within a gilt chain band, and small sprays of flowers and parrots on the rim.

The elaborate arms are of the Louthian family of Edinburgh and Overgogar, and the scene beneath the shield almost certainly illustrates the Firth of Forth. In the foreground is a milestone with the Roman numerals MDCCLXVIII – and undoubtedly this design was copied from the family bookplate of that date.

LITERATURE
Howard, *Chinese Armorial Porcelain*, p. 561.

## 95
## Plate

Qianlong, c.1785
Diameter: 9¼ in (23.4 cm)

Of octagonal shape with four scenic
panels on the rim interspersed with
ovals with classical urns; in the
centre a figure of Hope supporting
a coat of arms.

These scenic panels are unique to
this service, although the concept
they embody was much used by
European factories for figure
models. They represent the four
continents – Asia (pyramids, camels
and pagodas); Africa (elephants,
crocodiles and trading in beads);
America (Red Indian, tobacco plants
and buffalo); and Europe
(mercantile trade, guns and liberty).
The central arms are of Ker, with
Martin in pretence; possibly for
William Ker of Gateshaw, who
married his cousin Jane Martin, who
had a brother in the East India
Company (although there are other
marriages between these families).

The service was an elaborate one
with pierced fruit baskets and a
large tea service (much of which is
still together).

LITERATURE
Howard & Ayers, *China for the
West*, pp. 434–5 where a pierced
dish is illustrated and further
historical details are given.

## 96
### Dessert Plate
Qianlong, c.1785
Diameter: 7½ in (19.1 cm)

With blue-enamelled rim decorated with gilt husks, a chain band at the well and central armorial with name 'Morgan'.

This is one of two services made for the Morgan family of Hartford, Connecticut. The arms were recorded as Morgan of Boston in 1636, and of Flushing in 1693, and were those used by Sir Henry Morgan, Governor of Jamaica.

Two Hartford brothers and provincial merchants, John and Elias, had the two services made. This one, for John, brought back on the *Empress of China* in 1785, was followed on the next voyage by another with the full name 'Elias Morgan'.

This is one of the earliest personal services ordered specially from America after the opening of the trade directly with China.

LITERATURE
Howard, *Chinese Armorial Porcelain*, p. 747.
Howard, *New York and the China Trade*, p. 82 where both services are illustrated.

## 97
## Plate

Qianlong, c.1790
Diameter: 9 in (23 cm)

Decorated finely *en grisaille* with a country scene of two grazing cows at the edge of parkland.

This shows all the signs of being after an English amateur drawing, perhaps sent by the commissioner of the service. Although the rockwork and trees show Chinese influence, the scene is essentially European, and popular at that time as illustrating 'the country idyll'.

It is interesting that a later service, with a farmer leaning on a cow but showing more Chinese influence, was made about 1805 for the Morris family of Philadelphia, although there is no apparent link between these two services (see mugs no. 228).

## 98
## Plate

Jiaqing, c.1800
Diameter: 10 in (25 cm)

With a sparsely decorated rim in sepia with vine leaves and tendrils, and central design known as 'L'Urne Mystérieuse'.

This scene is after a print first published in 1793 in France, following a painting (possibly more than one) showing a young widow of France seated beside an urn decorated with fleur-de-lis and dolphins facing a serpent; the stem of the urn forming the outline of two faces (of Louis XVI and Marie Antoinette) and on either side of the weeping willow tree two more (of the Dauphin and Madame Royale).

This is one of at least five designs after this engraving ordered specially by émigrés in England (this one with the initials 'SDM'). Because of the variations, it is possible that some were ordered by china merchants for French clients in London. (The design survived for more than thirty years in porcelain and included a very similar engraving of about 1825 entitled 'Tombeau de Napoléon'!).

LITERATURE
Beurdeley, *Porcelain of the East India Companies*, pp. 106–7, another version, with engraving.
Howard & Ayers, *China for the West*, p. 247, different version.

## 100
## Plate

Jiaqing, c.1810
Diameter: 9¾ in (24.8 cm)

Decorated in pale salmon pink, sepia, crimson and gold, with a broad band of European design at the rim and a central river scene with trees and cliffs; with a European gentleman and his servant fishing on the near bank while two Chinese ladies stand on the further side.

Brancante recorded in 1950 that the service was bought by King John VI of Portugal and Brazil after he left Portugal with his court in the Napoleonic wars, and that Dr Simoens da Silva, in his catalogue of the Historical and Imperial Museum, reported that the service was formerly at the Imperial Estate at Santa Cruz. King John VI was King of Portugal and Brazil until his death in 1826.

LITERATURE
Brancante, *O Brasil e a Louça da India*, pp. 234–5.

## 99
## Hot Water Plate

Jiaqing, c.1805
Diameter: 10½ in (26.7 cm)

Circular, with square hot-water channel on one side and steam vent on the other. Decorated in underglaze blue with 'Fitzhugh' type decoration and central crest.

The use of four central sprays of flowers and antiques, combined with the butterfly and diaper border on the rim, can first be dated to about 1800, although both were essential parts of earlier designs from about 1760.

The name 'Fitzhugh' derives from Thomas FitzHugh, a director of the Hon. East India Company, who had a service made about 1780 displaying the four central panels (see chapters 2, 3).

The crest is of the Beale family. From 1798 to 1815 Thomas Beale, an Englishman, used his position as Prussian Consul in Canton to trade privately against the East India Company monopoly. In 1815 he was bankrupt after dealing in opium bonds.

LITERATURE
Howard, *Chinese Armorial Porcelain*, pp. 51–5 for a detailed explanation of the 'Fitzhugh' style and its derivation.

## 101

# Plate

Jiaqing, c.1810
Diameter: 9¾ in (24.7 cm)

Painted in uncharacteristic colours including a lime green, and with honeycomb diaper rim; the centre divided into four parts – two with fabulous animals and two with antiques. The pattern is known today as 'Bengal Tiger'.

The design mirrors closely the Worcester porcelain of that name of c.1770, and the Worcester porcelain is copied in turn from a late Kangxi pattern. An Atlanta private collection contains a Kangxi 'Bengal Tiger' saucer.

The particularly garish colours are not typical of either of the originals, and it is clear that this Chinese version of 'Bengal Tiger' was not long popular. It seems likely that it was ordered by a china shop in competition with Worcester.

LITERATURE
Simon Spero, *Worcester Porcelain*, pp. 83–4, a 1770 Worcester cup and saucer.

## 102
## Plate

Tongzhi, c.1865
Diameter: 8 in (20.2 cm)

Painted in the rich rose-pink and green enamels with gilding typical of Canton enamelling at that date. In the centre two crests and a motto surrounded by four oval cartouches – two with figures and two with birds.

The crests are of Macartney and Filgate; in 1862 Townley Macartney, a great-grandnephew of Earl Macartney who led the British Embassy to Pekin in 1792–3, assumed the additional name of Filgate under the will of his maternal grandfather.

In 1868 Daniel Ammen, an American East India Company captain, purchased for himself an exactly similar service with the initial 'A', another service with the cypher 'USG' – for the newly elected President Grant – and among a number of others, one for William Seward, Secretary of State under Lincoln.

All these have a central roundel for initials or crest, and the same four panels as on the service for Macartney-Filgate. It is clear that at that time it was possible for a captain to buy such a service direct from a merchant or china shop in Canton and take it with him on the return voyage, with the central roundel enamelled or gilded to his order.

LITERATURE
Howard & Ayers, *China for the West*, p. 442.
Feller, *The Canton Famille Rose Porcelain*, pp. 24–5.
Howard, *New York and the China Trade*, pp. 132–3 where the services for Grant, Seward and Ammen are illustrated.

103
## Dish

Guangxu, c.1880–1900
Diameter: $14\frac{3}{4}$ in (37.4 cm)

Decorated with six wedge-shaped panels, alternately with court scenes and flowers with exotic birds on a ground of green, red and gold scrollwork. In the centre a circular panel with the insignia 'V.O.C.'

This late enamelled dish mirrors in many respects the late 17th- and early 18th-century Chinese and Japanese dishes in underglaze blue, which bore the same insignia and frequently had the border divided into six panels (see no. 4).

It is possible that it was produced for the three-hundredth anniversary of the founding of the V.O.C. in 1602 (or for the centenary of its end in 1799).

# The Dinner Service: Other Pieces

## Examples, c.1640–c.1820

The dinner service as we know it today developed over more than two centuries, as new types of food became popular and social conventions changed.

Salts, for instance, were made in China from the start of the trade and mustard pots by the 1630s, while salad bowls were only made after 1790. Some special pieces, such as porcelain dish covers, have long since ceased to be made while sauce tureens and dessert baskets are seldom used today.

All the pieces had a function at the time, although some were certainly developed for their decorative effect.

THE DINNER SERVICE: OTHER PIECES

## 104
## Tureen Stand

Qianlong, c.1740
Width: 17 in (43.1 cm)

Heavily potted and of essentially rectangular form but with the ends indented and semi-circular, the rims thickly gadrooned after a silver original. The intricate decoration entirely in underglaze blue but with a central polychrome armorial.

The arms are of Pott (originally of Norfolk and London, and of a baronetcy which became extinct in 1732) with Clark in pretence; there is a similar service, made perhaps a

decade later, with the arms of Pott quartering Clarke, clearly for a son of the owner of this service.

The later Chinese service was sold at auction in London in 1957 – the tureen having boars'-head handles and being the same shape as the dish. It must be assumed that a similar tureen went with this dish and these are the only two recorded of this form.

In the best tradition of porcelain, the Mottahedeh Company of New York in the 1980s made a massive cheese dish and cover, the dish of exactly this shape and decoration, but with floral centre.

LITERATURE
Howard, *Chinese Armorial Porcelain*, p. 583 where a dish and tureen of the later service is illustrated.

## 105
## Soup Tureen

Qianlong, c.1750
Length: 14¾ in (37.3 cm)

Of oblong octagonal shape with flaring sides and stylized dragon handles, the cover with raised flat top and looped lotus finial. The decoration in underglaze blue with an armorial in enamels.

This tureen is an addition to the blue and white service with the same arms of Skinner made about twenty years earlier (no. 246). The dating of this pattern of tureen is aided by the Whitelock armorial service which is known to have been made about 1750. In 1730 few, if any, Chinese armorial tureens were part of services for British families – one of the earliest being for the service of c.1732 for George Best of Greenwich (whose brother was Commodore of the East India fleet).

In the previous year, the invoice of the large *famille rose* service for Sir Charles Peers, dated December 1731, lists only soup plates and soup *dishes*, for silver soup tureens were used almost exclusively until the 1730s.

The Skinner service was probably made for Mathew Skinner, who was Recorder of Oxford from 1721 and at the time of his death in 1749 Chief Justice of Chester.

LITERATURE
Howard, *Chinese Armorial Porcelain*, p. 271, Skinner service; p. 584 the Whitelock tureen.

## 106
## Tureen Stand

Qianlong, c.1755
Length: 14 in (35 cm)

Of long shaped octagonal form with simple rim design in sepia to simulate gadrooning, and in the centre a magnificent armorial of forty quarterings, with crest, crown and supporters.

The arms are of Frederick II (the Great), King of Prussia, who ruled from the death of his father in 1740 until 1786.

The service was ordered for him by the Königliche Preussische Asiatische Companie zu Emden and the arms are displayed in almost exactly this form in the *Wappen Calendar 1749*. It is recorded that a large part of the service was lost in the North Sea on the return journey.

LITERATURE
Le Corbeiller, *China Trade Porcelain*, pp. 80–3 where the tureen, and a plate of an earlier service, are illustrated.

## 107
## Soup Tureen
Qianlong, c.1755
Height: 14½ in (36.7 cm)

The rococo shape bordering on the grotesque and standing on heavy scroll feet with large applied scallops and finger scroll handles. The cover scalloped and rising irregularly to an inverted convolvulus finial with curling stem, the body painted with sprays of small European flowers.

This shape probably derived from silver – translated first into faience, and then made in porcelain by Paul Hannong in Strasbourg about 1750 and called *en baroque*. Attractive in its novelty, it was widely copied in Germany and Scandinavia, particularly by the Höchst factory, and undoubtedly a porcelain model must have been sent to China.

LITERATURE
Beurdeley, *Porcelain of the East India Companies*, p. 49, a Chinese armorial example and another in Delft. Howard & Ayers, *China for the West*, p. 552.

## 108

## Pair of Tureens and Stands

Qianlong, c.1755
Diameter of stand: 12½ in (31.6 cm)

Of circular form, with domed lids and half-moon chrysanthemum handles, decorated with floral sprays and armorials under a rich canopy.

This is a sumptuous service, made for an elegant small manor house for the Michel family, originally from Cornwall, but by the 17th century of Kingston Russell House in Dorset.

David-Robert Michel had married the daughter of a wealthy English merchant in Jamaica; his brother-in-law was Lancelot Lee of Coton, for whom was made the exceptional Lee service with scenes of the Pearl River and the River Thames (see no. 46).

LITERATURE
Howard, *Chinese Armorial Porcelain*, p. 489.

## 109

## Goose Soup Tureen

Qianlong, c.1760
Height: 16 in (40.6 cm)

Modelled in two pieces with the long neck intended as a handle, and the base of oval shape. The chest and base principally in rich golden brown enamel and the back with fanciful green, pink and golden brown feathers.

This is the more magnificent of two models of goose tureens, the other having similar plumage and shape but a much shorter neck. Although divided to allow the base to be used as a soup tureen, it may be doubted whether this often happened, as the base is shallow and impractical. The decorative effect, however, is considerable on a large dining table or sideboard. Sometimes these tureens had stands decorated with a

goose; while cockerels, ducks, boars'-heads, ox-heads and carp were also similarly modelled with attendant dishes. Only in rare armorial instances were they part of a service.

In 1763, the V.O.C. ordered twenty-five goose tureens, but it is likely that most were made for Private Trade (see chapter 3).

LITERATURE
Beurdeley, *Porcelain of the East India Companies*, p. 85, an armorial tureen.
Howard & Ayers, *China for the West*, pp. 590–1, long and short-necked tureens.

Sargent, *The Copeland Collection*, pp. 200–1, ox-head tureen; pp. 202–3, boar's-head tureen; pp. 209–11, cockerel tureen; pp. 212–15, carp tureens.

## 110

### Soup Tureen and Stand

Qianlong, c.1760
Length of tureen stand: 15½ in
(39.3 cm)

Of oblong octagonal form with
pomegranate finial and hare's-head
handles, decorated with *famille rose*
Chinese figures in a country
landscape, and bearing an armorial
on each piece.

This is the principal piece of a fine
service, one of only a dozen with
such a Chinese scene. It was ordered
by Captain Pinson Bonham who
was Master of the East Indiaman
*Norfolk* at Canton in 1757 and 1761.
He probably ordered this service for
himself, for there is another of
about 1765 with the arms of his
brother Samuel and his wife.

LITERATURE
Howard, *Chinese Armorial Porcelain*,
p. 345; ibid. p. 617 where a piece
from the Bonham impaling
Richardson service is illustrated.

## 111

### Pair of Soup Tureens

Qianlong, c.1760
Width: 9½ in (24.2 cm)

Of circular shape with high dome
and four panels of vertical
moulding, the finials being a plume
above radiating leaves and the
handles arched and close to the
body. Decorated with scattered
sprays of European flowers.

These unusual and specially ordered
tureens were after a European,
almost certainly continental, silver
form with the handles pressed
against the body to give strength

(rather than the more protruding
handles of the silver original).

The rococo-style armorial is of
Amyatt, an English family who
lived near Southampton, and it is
clear that a drawing or a model was
sent of these unusual tureens (see
also sauce boats no. 126).

LITERATURE
Howard, *Chinese Armorial Porcelain*,
p. 556.

## 112
## Soup Tureen

Qianlong, c.1765
Length: 13 in (33 cm)

Of oblong octagonal shape with moulded indentations at the corners, pomegranate finial and hare-head handles. The decoration has a peacock standing over his hen on floral rockwork. The finial in grass-green with patches of turquoise and pink.

This was a popular pattern of dinner service at the time, and rendered more popular because the Portuguese royal family owned a large service which was particularly favoured by King John VI (reigned 1816–26) and Queen Carlota, who were Prince Regent and Princess of Brazil during the King's mother's lifetime. (There is a tea service with portraits of Dom John and Dona Carlota Joaquina on separate pieces made in China about 1800, when he was Prince Regent.)

LITERATURE
Brancante, *O Brasil e a Louça da India*, pp. 222–3, 220–1 with the portrait tea service.

## 113
## Tureen

Qianlong, c.1765
Length: 13¾ in (35 cm)

Of simple oval shape, with high domed ogee cover and collared band near the top and crown-like finial; the handles of feathered headdress form. The decoration is of a floral garden terrace with two cockerels squabbling over a captive beetle.

Such tureens, made for the continental market, frequently have coronet finials (in this case the moulding on the finial has been painted with a leaf decoration but could equally well be painted as a coronet). The handles are a simplified form of others with a mask and upright feather headdress. The style was popular in Scandinavia, but copies Meissen, the original being in silver.

LITERATURE
Beurdeley, *Porcelain of the East India Companies*, p. 43, an earlier, more clearly European form illustrated, c.1735–40.
Howard & Ayers, *China for the West*, p. 552, a similar tureen with coronet finial.

## 114
## Tureen and Stand

Qianlong, c.1770
Length: 15 in (38 cm)

Of oval bombé shape, with cover of ogee form crowned by a rococo finial, the handles of feathered headdress shape. The cover, base and dish each decorated with eight panels divided by blue enamelled lines with naked European children dancing, the central ones in cartouches beneath a coronet.

This remarkable design, clearly ordered specially, has not been explained. The poses are not particularly erotic, although some of the originals might have been dancing girls.

The coronet is similar to that of a Dutch *burggraaf* (untitled nobleman) and the design, which is not armorial, shows every mark of an amateur drawing.

### 115
### Pair of Soup Tureens

Qianlong, c.1770
Width: 9 in (23 cm)

Of circular form with coronet finials and boar's-head handles, decorated with armorials and floral swags and tassels in *famille rose*.

The armorials are of de la Noue du Vair of Touraine in Brittany with his wife's coat accolé (a sailing ship with French ensigns). The family were created Comtes du Vair in 1653.

117

## 117
## Tureen Stand

Jiaqing, c.1810
Length: 15 in (45.6 cm)

Decorated in rich green translucent enamel over a black outline of the Fitzhugh pattern, with the central design replaced by an American eagle with widely spread wings, the motto '*E Pluribus Unum*', and on its breast a shield with initials 'AF'.

A number of pieces of this service are known but the original owner, 'AF', has not been identified. However, it must have been a particularly splendid service and it is surprising that it remains anonymous.

The wing span of the American eagle is impressive and the bird is more finely painted than almost all other porcelain with eagles. It seems likely that the design was planned in America and certainly ordered privately.

LITERATURE
Howard & Ayers, *China for the West*, p. 508–9 where a deep dish with special Chinese inscription on the reverse is illustrated.

## 116
## Tureen and Stand

Qianlong, c.1775
Width: 9½ in (24.2 cm)

Small, and of oval six-lobed form supported on three short cylindrical legs, the handles of chrysanthemum form and the cover shaped with pierced spherical finial. The decoration in underglaze blue with scenes of pagodas in a hilly wooded river landscape, the cover with formal floral decoration. With matching stand.

This is an unusual design in which Chinese and European influences mix. Clearly the Chinese must have been given a model for the shape, but not the painting.

## 118

# Tureen and Stand

Daoguang, c.1820

Length: $14\frac{1}{2}$ in (36.7 cm)

Of oval bombé shape with mushroom finial in orange and gold, the rest decorated with a black-outlined Fitzhugh decoration broadly painted in a rich translucent grass-green. The central medallion of the pattern superimposed with a crest within a ribbon with motto '*Laus Virtutis Actio*' ('the deed reinforces the virtue').

This is the tureen of the Rawson service; the private firm of Rawson & Company was one of seven British firms trading in Canton in the 1820s and 1830s. The family originated in South Yorkshire. A Chinese silver coffee pot with this crest was in the Mottahedeh Collection.

LITERATURE

Howard & Ayers, *China for the West*, p. 670, a Chinese silver coffee pot, c.1835, with this crest.

## 119
## Pair of Gosling and Single Duck Sauce Tureens

Qianlong, c.1760
Height: 7⅛ in (18.2 cm)

Modelled in the same manner as the goose soup tureen no. 109, these smaller tureens – presumably sauce tureens – are painted in a very similar manner with bright wing plumage.

As with the soup tureens, it is doubtful whether they were used often, and few are recorded with armorials. Their decorative effect accompanying the larger tureens is considerable.

LITERATURE
Sargent, *The Copeland Collection* where other smaller sauce tureens illustrated include elephants, pp. 206–9, and quail, pp. 204–5.

## 120
## Sauce Tureen and Stand

Qianlong, c.1770
Length of stand: 6½ in (16.5 cm)

Of shaped oblong octagonal form with rococo finial; decorated with stylized floral patterns based on pomegranates, hibiscus and variegated leaves – called today, for want of a better name, 'pseudo tobacco leaf'.

This is one of a number of 'tobacco leaf' and 'pseudo tobacco leaf' designs popular from about 1770 until the early 19th century and based largely on textile patterns that were imported also by the East India Companies.

This type of service may have been ordered by some East India Companies, but the large number of variations suggests that similar patterns were also available from china merchants in Canton (see also a pair of salts of slightly different pattern, no. 130).

LITERATURE
Howard & Ayers, *China for the West*, pp. 540–1 where three similar but slightly differing patterns of 'pseudo tobacco leaf' are illustrated.

## 121

# Pair of Sauce Tureens and Stands

Qianlong, c.1770

Length of stands: $7\frac{1}{2}$ in (19 cm)

Of oblong octagonal form with rococo finial and hare-head handles, decorated with a chain band and scattered flower sprays between armorials, and floral cartouches with the initials 'AS' (tureen in foreground) and 'CS' (behind).

These sauce tureens are from very similar services except for the initials and were made for two brothers – one for The Hon. Alexander Stewart who succeeded his two elder brothers as 10th Lord Blantyre in 1776; the other for his youngest brother, The Hon. Charles Stewart, who was in the East India Company and later served on the Supreme Council of Bengal. (See no. 77 for a plate from the service for their elder brother.)

LITERATURE
Howard, *Chinese Armorial Porcelain*, p. 576.

## 123
## Cover (on dish)

Yongzheng, c.1725
Width: $9\frac{1}{2}$ in (24.3 cm)

Very heavily potted, of domed shape with moulded lip and large ball finial on pedestal. The outside finely painted with bands of *rouge-de-fer* and gold and a crest among *famille verte* sprays; the inside as elaborately painted with large sprays of flowers and fruit in *famille verte* enamels, and a wide band of octagonal rose-pink diaper inside the rim. The octagonal dish of exactly the same period with heavy flat base, but with a different armorial.

These massive and impractical covers were designed for the thickly potted dishes illustrated and were part of a very small number of dinner services with such covers. The crest is of Sayer, and the arms on the full service are of Sayer quarterly; made for a son of Exton Sayer, MP for Tottenham, who married Catherine Talbot. It is no coincidence that the only other armorial examples of covers known are for Charles Talbot, his uncle, created Lord Talbot, and ancestor of the present Earls of Shrewsbury.

LITERATURE
Howard, *Chinese Armorial Porcelain*, p. 200.

## 122
## Sauce Tureen and Stand

Jiaqing, c.1810
Length: tureen $7\frac{5}{8}$ in (19.4 cm);
stand $8\frac{1}{8}$ in (20.6 cm)

Of oval bombé shape with large mushroom finial; the cover, tureen and stand decorated in orange Fitzhugh pattern, with the central design replaced by an eagle in sepia with widely spread wings and on its breast a shield with initials 'BSP'.

As with the soup tureen stand of this pattern in green Fitzhugh (see no. 117) the identity of 'BSP' is unknown.

## 124
## Sauceboat

Qianlong, c.1750
Length: $8\frac{1}{4}$ in (21 cm)

With oval base, slightly waisted, rising to a moulded wavy rim stretching from a lower turned-over spout to a higher arched handle; decorated in underglaze blue with floral patterns, the glaze worn.

From the salvaged cargo of the *Geldermalsen*, which sank January 1752, and, as with all sauceboats (which were a European form unfamiliar to the Chinese), copying in simplified outline a silver original, in this case of the 1740s. Earlier, and occasionally later, boats had double handles, and a few had impractical covers.

The sauceboat could be ordered separately but by this time was almost always part of a dinner service, as was the case on the *Geldermalsen* where no single sauceboats are mentioned in the manifest, although a considerable number were found.

LITERATURE
Jörg, *The Geldermalsen*, pp. 62–3.

125
Sauceboat

Qianlong, c.1755
Length: 7½ in (19.1 cm)

Of boat shape, rising from an oval base, with protruding spouts at either end and looped handles on either side in the centre; under each lip an armorial.

This is a later adaptation of the two-handled sauceboats made after silver shapes of the first three decades of the century.

The arms are of Hale impaling Dissert. General John Hale of Guisborough in Yorkshire, who bore these arms, had twenty-one children of whom a number were in the East India Company, but his relationship with the John Hale who married about 1750 and who left in his will 'my china stampt with my arms and those of my wife Jane' to his niece Mary is uncertain.

LITERATURE
Howard, *Chinese Armorial Porcelain*, p. 367.

126
Pair of Sauceboats

Qianlong, c.1760
Length: 8¼ in (21 cm)

Of scalloped form rising from an oval base, with the lip protruding, and the handle of strap form overhanging the body; under the lip an armorial between flower sprays.

Although these boats were made for the Amyatt family who lived near Southampton, the silver original from which they are copied is probably continental, matching in this respect the Amyatt tureens illustrated (no. 111).

LITERATURE
Howard, *Chinese Armorial Porcelain*, p. 556.

## 127
## Pair of Salts

Kangxi, c.1715
Width: $3\frac{1}{8}$ in (8 cm)

Of circular waisted form, with ribbed moulding on the body and lip to simulate gadrooning. The body painted in *famille verte* translucent enamels with sprays of flowers, and the scalloped dish with a lily plant in *rouge-de-fer* and gold.

The salt-cellar was a vessel of entirely western significance and unlike most other forms which existed in some form in China, all salts were copied from European patterns, almost all of silver – in this case of c.1700. At this time they were ordered separately, and only much later as part of a dinner service. In Europe it was normal to buy sets of up to eight salts for a dinner table.

## 128
## Pair of Salts

Qianlong, c.1750
Width: $3\frac{3}{8}$ in (8.7 cm)

Of hexagonal section rising to a six-lobed rim with shallow saucer; the painting in underglaze blue with diaper at base and rim and a glimpse of a river scene with buildings on the top. The glaze dull.

These salts were part of the cargo of the Dutch ship *Geldermalsen* which sank in the South China Seas in January 1752; the cargo was salvaged by Captain Michael Hatcher and sold in Amsterdam in 1986.

They matched the largest services (at auction called 'lattice fence') which had been originally ordered in sizes of about 160 pieces including four salts, but were supplied in smaller numbers. The orders were direct from the directors in Holland and the shipping invoice records 171 dinner services in all, without full details.

LITERATURE
Jörg, *The Geldermalsen*, pp. 60–2.

## 129
## Pair of Salts

Qianlong, c.1755
Length: 3 in (7.6 cm)

Of elongated octagonal form after a later silver form known as 'trencher salts'; painted in *famille rose* enamels on the sides with flower sprays above a spearhead border, on the top an armorial with the motto 'Snug'.

The arms are those of Hare and were first granted to Sir Nicholas Hare, twice Speaker of the House of Commons in Elizabethan times. Although there was a Baronetcy, extinct in 1764, and later the Irish Earldom of Listowel with the same arms, it is not certain for whom this service was made. The motto is not recorded or explained.

LITERATURE
Howard, *Chinese Armorial Porcelain*, p. 450.

## 130
## Pair of Salts

Qianlong, c.1770
Length: 3 in (7.6 cm)

Of elongated octagonal 'trencher' form with scalloped rim after silver, painted with flower sprays and tobacco leaves in underglaze blue and *famille rose*, and with a Chinese maiden punting on a large floating floral leaf.

This is perhaps the earliest and most charming of the tobacco leaf patterns, which were to develop slowly over the next few decades into all-over patterns of highly coloured leaves (see no. 251).

131
Salt

Qianlong, c.1795
Length: 4 in (10.2 cm)

Oval, and decorated with blue
enamel picked out in gold with a
husk chain at base, an enamelled
band with gold stars on the rim, and
a finely painted blue floral spray
with gold in the centre. On the
reverse the initials 'JA' in an oval
medallion.

Almost a century after the *famille
verte* salts illustrated above (no. 127),
this form still copies the shape of
European (by now sometimes
porcelain) salts of the period.
Experience must have shown that
arms and initials could quickly
become worn on the top surface
and these were more conveniently,
but less artistically, painted on the
sides.

## 132
## Mustard Pot

Chongzhen, c.1640
Height: 5¼ in (13 cm)

Of hexagonal section and ovoid form rising from a pedestal foot and with an ample handle, the cover domed with a short hollow tubular finial; a 19th-century metal hinge joining the handle and cover. Painted in underglaze blue with floral sprays above lappets on the foot.

A number of such mustard pots of exactly this design were in the cargo of a Chinese junk salvaged in 1983 and sold in Amsterdam in 1984, which also contained two (unrelated) pieces with the cyclical date for 1643.

Volker reports a V.O.C. order of 1639 for 200 mustard pots of which half are to be 'ribbed as sample' and illustrates one of this form.

LITERATURE
Volker, *Porcelain and the Dutch East India Company*, p. 43, illustration no. 20.
Christie's Amsterdam, catalogue, 14 March 1984, Lots 104–5, very similar round pots.

## 133
## Mustard Pot

Kangxi, c.1695
Height: 4½ in (11.5 cm)

Of globular form on a collared stem with protruding handle, the cover high domed with double knop finial. Painted all over on three spiral panels with fishermen in river landscapes, the glaze dull.

This was one of three types of mustard pot in the cargo of a Chinese trading vessel which sank off the Vung Tau peninsula in c.1695, another being globular with no foot, and the third having a shallow cover with seated dog.

Mustard pots were ordered by the Dutch company as early as 1608 in quantities of up to a thousand at a time, and this continued throughout the century.

LITERATURE
Christie's Amsterdam, catalogue, 7–8 April 1992; Lots 228–46 (58 in all) illustrated p. 41.

## 135
## Two Sweetmeat Stands

Qianlong, c.1765
Width: 7¼ in (18.5 cm)

Modelled as three scallops with a central handle in the form of a dolphin, each scallop with a different spray of *famille rose* flowers; the dolphin in iron red, black and gold.

The idea was probably first produced at Bow in England about 1755, and later examples were made about this period at Worcester, Derby and by Bonnin & Morris in Philadelphia.

Although normally called a sweetmeat dish, the trays could have been used for spices. Undoubtedly this was part of a private order.

LITERATURE
Howard & Ayers, *China for the West*, p. 568 where a very similar example is illustrated.

## 134
## Cruet Set

Qianlong, c.1755
Height (jugs in stand): 5½ in (14.1 cm)

The holder formed of two hexagonal trays with looped handle between them; the baluster jugs of hexagonal section with covers and similar handles. All pieces decorated with sprays of *famille rose* flowers.

Cruet sets were made in underglaze blue and Chinese Imari palette as early as the late 17th century, at that time with larger round trays – sometimes three joined. It is assumed that the jugs contained oil and vinegar (17th-century Japanese examples are sometimes marked 'O' and 'A' – for oil and vinegar).

They were made both as parts of dinner services (as armorial examples attest) and separately, although the numbers known are not great.

## 136
## Pair of Herring Dishes

Qianlong, c.1765
Length: $9\frac{1}{4}$ in (23.5 cm)

Of shaped rectangular form and
decorated in underglaze blue with a
fish within a formal border edged
with honeycomb diaper. On the
reverse, eight groups of four dots.

These dishes were used for herring,
particularly in Holland, and perhaps
the fish is intended to be one,
although more tropical in
appearance. The shape derives from
similar Delft dishes painted with
fish, although there is no exact
original known.

LITERATURE
Howard & Ayers, *China for the
West*, p. 85 where a Delft dish is also
illustrated.

## 137
## Sweetmeat Dish

Qianlong, c.1755
Width: 4⅝ in (11.7 cm)

Of small moulded wavy heart shape, decorated in underglaze blue with a plain band at the rim, and a seaside central scene with jetty, small sailing ships and a building across the river.

Because of the collection of similar porcelain at Burghley House, Gordon Lang was able to point to the unusual chain of commerce that produced these small dishes, which in groups would form a supper set.

Following drawings in the manner of the Dutch painter Van Frytom on Delft pottery (see no. 11), small dishes of this and similar shapes were made in Japan c.1700. About 1752 a number were copied at Bow (including this pattern), and soon after that the Chinese copied the Bow models, probably quite unaware of the Japanese and Delft predecessors.

LITERATURE
Lang, *The Wrestling Boys (Chinese and Japanese Ceramics at Burghley House)*, pp. 11–15 where Japanese and Bow originals of this design are illustrated.

## 138
## Two Sweetmeat Dishes

Jiaqing, c.1798
Length: 4⅛ in (10.5 cm)

Of deep uneven wedge shape with ribbed base, finely painted within a blue-enamelled rim with an elaborate quarterly coat of arms.

These dishes are part of a supper set – originally eight of wedge shape, probably to be arranged round an octagonal central dish – and supplied in a wooden case.

The arms are of James (Beveridge) Duncan, who took the name of Duncan on inheriting the estate of Galloford from his Duncan cousin in 1798. He was also a cousin of the famous Admiral Duncan, the victor of Camperdown in 1797.

LITERATURE
Howard, *Chinese Armorial Porcelain*, p. 1001.

## 139
## Strainer and Dish

Qianlong, c.1760
Width of dish: 10 in (25.4 cm)

The strainer and dish both with scalloped edge and moulded cartouches on the rim, the strainer pierced in an elaborate pattern and standing on three short stump feet. The four floral rim cartouches within a scattering of tiny floral sprays about a shell cartouche enclosing a cobweb, below which the motto *Interrupta Retexam*.

This is part of an elaborate service exactly copying a Meissen original, all pieces with similar decoration but bearing a large number of different pseudo armorials with mottoes. In spite of considerable research, their meaning remains obscure, but it is thought that they could have Jesuit significance. Much of the service was sold by General Sir George Burns at North Mimms Park in the 1980s and may have come from his great-uncle, Mr J. Pierpont Morgan, but it is doubtful if either had any idea of their origin.

The plate and strainer were introduced by Meissen, probably for lettuce, which had been credited with mild medicinal powers since the 16th century and gained popularity in the 18th century.

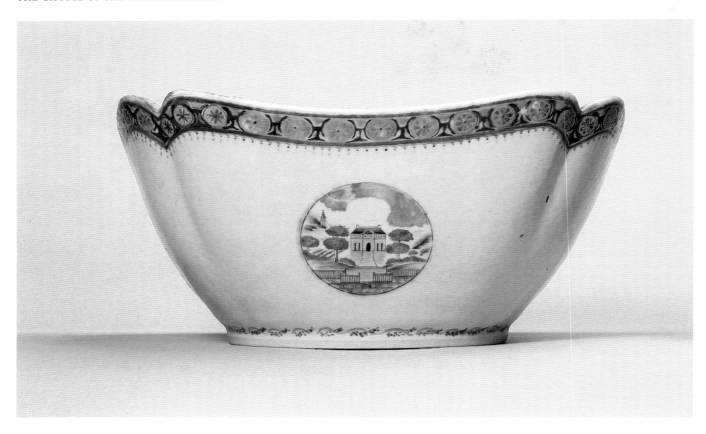

## 140
### Salad Bowl

Jiaqing, c.1815
Width: $9\frac{3}{4}$ in (24.8 cm)

Of square form rising from a circular base and with indented corners, this bowl has a broad band of bright blue and yellow diaper at the rim; on either side, divided by flower sprays, is a roundel of a country house, with open driveway and crops in the foreground.

Bowls of this shape were frequently used for salad rather than punch and the form did not appear in Chinese porcelain until about 1790. The scene and rim decoration suggest the South American market, which was a considerable one in the early 19th century. The painting of the house could be after an amateur watercolour rather than an engraving.

## 141
### Two Butter Tubs

Qianlong, c.1750
Width: $4\frac{1}{2}$ in (11.5 cm)

Of shallow cylindrical body with string moulding at foot and lip and two arched and pierced loops; the covers slightly domed with long low straight handles and slots cut to allow for the loops. The underglaze blue decoration with an all-over pattern of scrolling leaves and flowers.

Circular and oval butter tubs had been made earlier at Delft and later at Meissen since the 1730s, and the loops and handles imitated traditional wooden milk tubs with loops for a carrying cord. Although these are unusual objects, they had been ordered by the Dutch company and were part of the 1751 *Geldermalsen* cargo salvaged in 1985. In fact the salvage included round

and oval butter tubs, in all 235 in seven different forms or decorations (40 more than the shipping invoice!).

Butter tubs were occasionally part of dinner services and the blue and white Valckenier service (see no. 247) has armorial butter tubs.

LITERATURE
Jörg, *The Geldermalsen*, pp. 86–7.

## 142
## Butter Tub

Qianlong, c.1785
Width: $5\frac{1}{4}$ in (13.4 cm)

Of circular shape, with the wavy rim overhanging the base and the domed cover with strawberry finial resting inside. Decorated at the rim with gold trellis and wavy husk chain, with an armorial on a blue mantle lined with red.

This probably copies a German shape and the arms are related to, if not those of, Premrau von Premerstein of Austria, who became Chevaliers of the Empire in 1783, but who are recorded with a different crest.

## 143
## Lemon Basket and Stand
Qianlong, c.1765
Height: 15 in (38 cm)

Modelled naturalistically as a tree stump with two putti reaching round it, with a separate shaped moulded oval basket on the top. The trunk and putti in natural colours and a painted spray of flowers in the basket.

This exactly follows a Meissen original, first produced in the 1740s as a table centrepiece, round which shaped bowls were fitted on a porcelain tray. The top basket was more usually pierced after about 1770.

In 1787–8 a similar example was made for Major Samuel Shaw bearing the Order of Cincinnatti, documenting a forty-year popularity for this elaborate form.

LITERATURE
Scheurleer, *Chinese Export Porcelain*, pl. 157.
Howard & Ayers, *China for the West*, pp. 564 (where the basket has an armorial inside), 566.

## 144

## Three Fruit Baskets and Stands

Qianlong, c.1770
Length of stands: $11\frac{1}{4}$ in (28.6 cm)
and $8\frac{1}{2}$ in (21.8 cm)

The baskets of shaped oval form with flaring rims and looped upright handles, the body pierced with radiating diamonds between moulded flowers; each having a matching stand. Painted with armorials and scattered flowers.

The idea for fruit baskets derived from the table centrepieces devised at Meissen from about 1740. The piercing and moulding had developed on the Continent and at English factories, and in the Chinese examples is hand-cut.

The arms are those illustrated by Rolland as Rees van Tets of Holland, and the service is an elaborate one including fruit coolers.

LITERATURE
Howard & Ayers, *China for the West*, pp. 564–6 where similar piercing is illustrated on other shapes.

## 146
## Chestnut Basket

Qianlong, c.1785
Width: 10 in (25.4 cm)

In the form of a deep pierced covered circular dish on pedestal foot, with cross-woven handles and open chestnut finial. The piercing of alternating slits of Chinese design, and with unusual painted bands of medallions.

This form probably originated from English creamware patterns, but the hand-cut piercing is Chinese in design. With centrepieces and fruit baskets, these baskets formed part of the new 'ritual' of eating fruit in the late 18th century. It is likely that this shape was ordered as a part of a dessert service.

LITERATURE
Phillips, *China Trade Porcelain*, p. 129 where an armorial example of this shape is illustrated. Howard & Ayers, *China for the West*, p. 585 where another example is illustrated.

## 145
## Shaped Dish

Jiaqing, c.1810
Width: 7¾ in (19.8 cm)

Of square 'cushion' shape with rounded corners and incurving sides, decorated in the centre with European flowers in a roundel and encircled by a pattern of shaped floral panels in blue enamels picked out in gold.

This dish formed part of a dessert service similar to those made in a number of English factories, with shaped oval, kidney-shaped and square dishes and baskets raised on pedestals, which together with fruit coolers created a sumptuous effect at this stage of a dinner – and at other times was merely for display.

The original of this pattern was almost certainly Coalport porcelain of about 1805, and the Chinese version would have been ordered as part of a service in competition with English ware.

## 147
## Dessert Plate

Qianlong, c.1795
Diameter: 7 in (17.8 cm)

With finely painted *famille rose* centre of three ladies on a rocky terrace, the well in puce enamel scale pattern with eight alternating scenic and bird cartouches; outside the reticulated rim, a border of tight gilt scrollwork with eight further cartouches.

This dessert plate is of a late Qianlong style of the highest quality, known in the 20th century as 'Palace ware' and more recently as 'Rockefeller ware' after Nelson Rockefeller, who collected it.

Each piece has a different scene of courtiers and ladies, many with country temples in a palace-like garden. A small number of very fine services were ordered between 1795 and 1800 by the families of Drummond and Stirling of Keir, in particular by Andrew John Drummond, who was a General in the East India Company and visited Canton in the 1790s (and who unsuccessfully petitioned for the restoration of the Strathallan title 'under attainder' since the 1745 Jacobite Rising). His son, James Drummond, was President of the Select Committee at Canton from 1801 to 1807.

LITERATURE
Howard & Ayers, *China for the West*, pp. 188–9, a tureen and plate with different scenes.

# The Tea and Coffee Set

Examples, c.1640–c.1805

Tea was drunk regularly in Europe from the second quarter of the 17th century,* and the vessels used for this oriental beverage were no doubt those which the Chinese were accustomed to use themselves. It was not until the second half of the 18th century, however, that to meet European preferences the Chinese bowls acquired handles and became cups.

The European 'tea sett' comprised a teapot, teapoy (or tea caddy), milk jug (sometimes both for hot and cold milk), sugar bowl (with cover), slop bowl and small trays for pot and spoon (which, until the mid-18th century, was handed round for stirring). Since many tea sets had matching coffee sets, two lots of cups were usually supplied with one lot of saucers.

Coffee and chocolate, which were not oriental drinks, were also popular from the 17th century and were drunk from beakers or, more usually, cups with handles. It is clear from contemporary pictures that saucers were not always used when drinking chocolate. Undoubtedly some 'coffee cups' were used for chocolate, but early records (see chapter 3) mention 'handle chocolatettes'.

*See Volker, *Porcelain and the Dutch East India Company . . . 1602–1682*, 1954, p. 48: 'The habit of drinking tea was now forming in Europe, where it was started by the Dutch, who had heard about tea for the first time from Van Linschoten's *Itinerario* in 1596. In 1607 they carried tea from Macao to Bantam, the first recorded shipment of tea by any Europeans stationed in East Asia. The first recorded shipment to Europe was in 1610, when the Company bought tea in Hirado and shipped it home via Bantam. Occasional shipments will have reached Holland from this year onward, and on January 2, 1637 the Directors wrote to Batavia: "As tea begins to come into use by some of the people, we expect some jars of Chinese as well as Japanese tea with every ship". As a result of this tea-cups were now in stronger demand. Though a few times before this they appear in the bills of lading, they were till now only an Asian trade name for a special kind of small cups not used in Europe for tea. In this year 25,000 are ordered. After this year tea-cups form a more or less constant item in the Company's porcelain trade.'

| 148 | Tea or coffee urn |
| 149–66 | Teapots |
| 167–74 | Coffee (or chocolate) pots |
| 175–76 | Teapot stands |
| 177–78 | Spoon trays |
| 179–82 | Teapoys |
| 183–88 | Milk jugs |
| 189–92 | Sugar bowls |
| 193–213 | Beakers, teabowls and coffee cups and saucers. |

## 148
## Tea or Coffee Urn

Japanese, c.1700
Height: 16 in (40.6 cm)

Of moulded pear shape with fluted bulbous band below the cover, standing on three tall feet in the form of figures. The body moulded with cranes and vegetation; the short handle of square section and the flat cover with tall tear-shaped finial. The painting in Japanese Imari palette with underglaze blue, iron-red and other enamels. A pewter tap with fan-shaped handle, added in Europe.

Such urns could be used either for tea or coffee; the overall shape is adapted from Dutch silver but liberally embellished in Japanese style, and almost certainly for the Dutch market.

The form is one of the more ambitious adaptations from metalware and the idea seems only to have been tried in Japan – perhaps because it proved expensive and clumsy.

LITERATURE
Howard & Ayers, *China for the West*, pp. 128–9 where a Dutch silver urn of similar shape is illustrated.

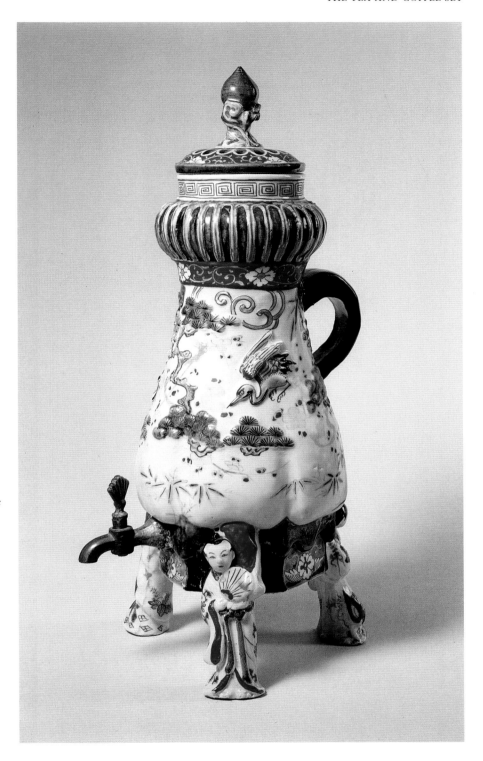

## 150
## 'Cadogan' Winepot
Chongzhen, c.1640
Height: 6 in (15.2 cm)

In the form of a peach resting on a short pedestal foot, with handle and spout resembling a stem attached by leaves; the base with an open tube running to near the top for filling. Decorated in underglaze blue, with fruit and leaves incorporating some formal trellis. From the first Hatcher Cargo, also with glaze dulled.

Filled from the base and without lid, this form of winepot could, in theory, have been used for tea, but it is much more likely that examples that were bought were only displayed as curiosities on arrival in Europe. The name 'Cadogan' was given to such pots in the early 19th century, when the then Earl of Cadogan promoted their use as teapots and, at his instigation, the shape was made by the Rockingham factory.

LITERATURE
Sheaf & Kilburn, *The Hatcher Porcelain Cargoes*, p. 64.
Christie's Amsterdam, catalogue, 14 March 1984, lot 422 and other designs of such winepots Lots 417–8.

## 149
## Winepot or Teapot
Chongzhen, c.1640
Height: 9½ in (24.3 cm)

Of inverted pear shape with domed cover and cylindrical collared finial, the spout curved and the rectangular handle standing upwards on the shoulders. The painting in underglaze blue with floral sprays, and a band of floral scrollwork on the shoulders. The glaze dull.

This wine pot, sold by Captain Hatcher in 1984, was part of a cargo from a Chinese vessel salvaged in the South China Seas. The cargo contained two lids with the cyclical date of 1643 and all the porcelain was of a similar date.

In China this vessel may have been a wine or a tea pot, but in the very early formative days of tea drinking (the habit had scarcely been established a decade in Europe) various shapes of teapots were offered, and it wasn't until the later 17th century that the form common today was eventually chosen.

LITERATURE
Christie's Amsterdam, catalogue, 14 March 1984, Lots 186–91, seven similar 'winepots.'

## 151
## Teapot

Chongzhen, c.1640
Height: 5 in (12.7 cm)

Of hexagonal baluster form with curved spout and the cylindrical finial double-ringed. The decoration in underglaze blue with each of the four side panels with the figure of an immortal, the handle and spout with stylized clouds, and on the base a *fu* mark (for good fortune). Glaze dull. From the first Hatcher Cargo.

One of the most sophisticated teapots in this cargo among more than twenty different shapes and sizes. Clearly the Dutch merchants in Batavia could select those which they thought would be most fashionable.

LITERATURE
Sheaf & Kilburn, *The Hatcher Porcelain Cargoes*, p. 64, where this teapot is illustrated.

## 152
## Teapot

Chongzhen, c.1640
Height: 4 in (10.2 cm)

Of globular form and decorated in underglaze blue with leaves and blossom on boughs. The cover with more formal scrollwork and flowers, the tall cylindrical finial white and double-ribbed. The glaze dull. From the first Hatcher Cargo, sunk c.1643.

This more standard shape of pot was possibly intended only for tea from the outset (see nos 149–51).

LITERATURE
Sheaf & Kilburn, *The Hatcher Porcelain Cargoes*, pp. 64–5 where other teapots are illustrated.

## 153
## Teapot

Japanese, c.1700
Height: $7\frac{1}{4}$ in (18.4 cm)

Of octagonal globular form with curving spout and simple handle, the cover slightly domed with flat knop finial. The decoration in underglaze blue, with two shaped oval Chinese scenes after European engravings separated by panels of white scrollwork on a blue ground (the side not seen has temples on a rocky headland above a lake with boats – perhaps at the Summer Palace).

This form was common in smaller Yixing Chinese stoneware teapots of that period. The scenes are from engravings by Dr Olfred Dapper in *Gedenkwaardig Bedrijf der Nederlandsche Oost-Indische Maatschappye op de kust en in het Keizerrijk van Taising of Sina* – the story of the Dutch Embassy to Peking in the early 1660s – and that illustrated is a shortened view of the Embassy approaching Peking.

Made for the Dutch market and ordered through their factory on Deshima Island in Nagasaki Bay. The disruption caused by the fall of the Ming Dynasty in 1644 caused a considerable part of the Dutch trade to be transferred to Japan and this depot, though proving ever more expensive, was still open in the late 1730s when a small number of Pronk designs were ordered there.

LITERATURE
Lang, *The Wrestling Boys* (catalogue of an Exhibition at Burghley House 1983), pp. 11–15 illustrate Japanese porcelain after European engravings or drawings of this date.

## 154
## Teapot

Kangxi, c.1710
Height: 5 in (12.7 cm)

Of quadrangular ovoid form, with
square lid and moulded finial,
square section handle and spout.
The underglaze blue decoration
copies a European engraving and
shows on each side a mermaid
among reeds with a large fish rising
in a pond.

The original, an engraving of 1676
by S. Le Clerc, illustrates the story
of Dirce – one of Venus's less
successful rivals who, as a
punishment for rivalling her in
beauty, was turned into a mermaid
and made to fall in love with a carp.

A small number of these teapots are
known and the design was clearly
specially commissioned – possibly
even including the shape of the
teapot to accommodate a
rectangular engraving.

LITERATURE
Hervouët & Bruneau, *La Porcelaine
des Compagnies des Indes à Décor
Occidental*, p. 309 where a similar
teapot in the Groninger Museum is
illustrated.
D'Isaac de Benserade, *Les
Metamorphoses d'Ovide en rondeaux*,
1676, illustration by S. Le Clerc.

## 155
## Teapot

Kangxi, c.1710
Height: $3\frac{1}{2}$ in (8.9 cm)

In the form of a short bundle of bamboo with bamboo handle and twisted spout, all decorated in *famille verte* enamels with chrysanthemum, peony, daisies and cockerels.

This unusual form of teapot was both practical and novel, but its popularity was short-lived and the form is not known in *famille rose*, although not uncommon in Yixing ware.

It is typical of the unusual forms available from Chinese merchants which would appeal to some supercargoes, but it would have been much more expensive to produce than the globular pots and this may explain in part its short popularity.

## 156
## 'Cadogan' Teapot

Kangxi, c.1720
Height: 6 in (15.2 cm)

Of peach-shaped body resting on a short pedestal foot, with spout and handle of teapot shape of the period. The body in iron-red with floral scrollwork in white; the foot in *famille verte* green enamel with white prunus blossom on 'cracked ice'.

The popularity of this strange shape, as a curiosity as much as a practical teapot, had survived for at least eighty years and was, a century later, to be copied at the Rockingham factory (see no. 150).

It seems most probable that a small demand for this shape in Europe was met by supercargoes as part of their private trade.

## 157
## Teapot

Yongzheng, c.1725
Length: 7 in (17.8 cm)

Of plain globular form with straight spout and pointed finial; decorated with bands of *rouge-de-fer* and gold scrollwork, with *famille verte* groups of antiques and flowers and a large armorial.

The arms are of Bolney, a family with branches in three southern counties of England – Berkshire, Suffolk and Sussex (where there is a village of that name). As well as an armorial dinner and tea service, the family ordered a set of mother-of-pearl counters with arms engraved exactly as on the porcelain.

LITERATURE
Howard, *Chinese Armorial Porcelain*, p. 208.

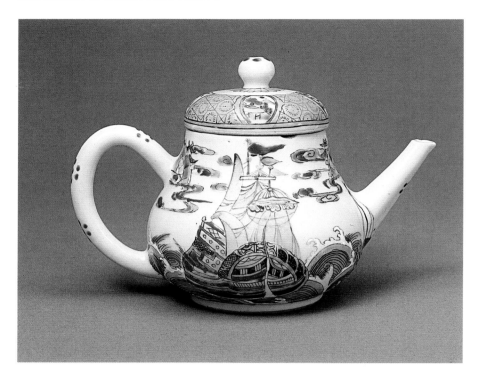

## 158
## Teapot

Yongzheng, c.1730
Height: $4\frac{1}{8}$ in (10.6 cm)

Of pear shape with short straight spout and domed cover with moulded finial. Decorated in *rose verte* enamels with a barely recognizable European merchant vessel (see illustration no. 35).

There are fewer tea set pieces than plates known. The latter may have been intended only for display.

LITERATURE
Howard & Ayers, *China for the West*, p. 218 where this teapot is illustrated.

## 159
## Teapot

Yongzheng, c.1735
Height: 4 in (10.2 cm)

Of globular form, with the concave fluted moulded panels on the cover matched on the base, which has applied aquatic plants. Decorated in *famille rose* with a boy on a water buffalo in a landscape, with flowers and rockwork above the fluting.

The period 1730 to 1740 saw a considerable number of such shaped teapots, with finely painted cups and saucers, sometimes with similar bases. They were not mass produced but individual services which would have been chosen from stock in china shops in Canton. It is likely that many were destined only for display in china cabinets, and surviving pieces are frequently in excellent condition.

LITERATURE
Howard & Ayers, *China for the West*, p. 157 where a teapot of lotus form has a similar base.

## 160
## Teapot

Qianlong, c.1745
Height: 4½ in (11.5 cm)

Of globular form, resting on a
pedestal foot and with curved spout
and flat lid with waisted cylindrical
finial. The floral decoration in rich
*famille rose* and a well painted
armorial using silver and gold
enamels.

The arms are of Abercromby and
this pot has a history of being
formerly in the possession of 'Sir
George Abercromby' – but there is
more than one!

The pot offers an unusual and early
example of influence by English,
probably Staffordshire, pottery and
the shape must have been specially
ordered.

## 161
## Teapot

Qianlong, c.1750
Height: $5\frac{1}{4}$ in (14 cm)

Of globular form with tear-shaped finial, decorated all over with white enamel *bianco-sopra-bianco* flowers. Over this a scattering of butterflies, caterpillars, insects and European flowers.

While the *bianco-sopra-bianco* is Chinese, the insects and butterflies were painted in Europe, probably in London. The style of the teapot is of the period 1740 to 1750 but the overpainting rather later, and this could suggest a clearing of old and difficult-to-sell stock in China of the rather unexciting white floral pattern. An enterprising merchant could well have bought a quantity of such teapots inexpensively and sold them to the English decorating workshops.

## 162
## Teapot

Qianlong, c.1751
Length: 9 in (23 cm)

Of bullet shape with flat cover, bud finial, straight spout and shaped handle. Decorated in underglaze blue with willow tree and peony on a foreshore, with small buildings on a rocky island. The glaze excellent.

The shape is simplified from Meissen and derived from silver, and is the most sophisticated type of teapot salvaged from the Dutch East Indiaman *Geldermalsen* by Captain Hatcher, and auctioned in Amsterdam in 1986.

There were 200 of this pattern sold (and 75 others of the shape with enamels) and it is clear that this design was being purchased in bulk by the Dutch company. The almost perfect state of the glaze after some 233 years under water is due to the close packing, and the discovery of these cases almost undisturbed in the hull of the ship, embedded in the cargo of tea.

LITERATURE
Jörg, *The Geldermalsen*, p. 70.
Sheaf & Kilburn, *The Hatcher Porcelain Cargoes*, p. 143.
Christie's Amsterdam, catalogue, 28 April, 2 May 1986, Lots 2078–2148.

## 163
## Teapot

Qianlong, c.1760
Height: 5¼ in (14 cm)

Of globular form with lotus–petal moulding on body and cover; the painting in tones of pink with shading, and on either side a circular panel with a gilded scrolling lotus flower.

The lotus petal was a particularly popular theme in the decorating of Export porcelain throughout the mid–18th century. While individual supercargoes ordered such services, it seems likely that larger consignments would have been ordered by the East India companies. There were a number of variations of the pattern and pieces of five similar tea and chocolate services are at Melford Hall in Suffolk, captured by Captain Hyde Parker from the Spanish treasure ship *Santissima Trinidad* off Manila in October 1762.

LITERATURE
Gordon, *Chinese Export Porcelain*, pl. VII.

## 165
## Teapot

Qianlong, c.1780
Height: 4¾ in (12.2 cm)

Of plain drum shape after a silver form, with slightly raised flat cover and strawberry finial, and crossed strap handles with vine ends. The porcelain particularly white, and finely painted with flower sprays and a coat of arms in *famille rose* enamels, silver and gold.

The arms are of Frederick Ginkel, 5th Earl of Athlone, whose family had had an earlier Chinese armorial dinner service made about 1760. This tea and dessert service (no dinner plates are recorded) is much more finely painted than the dinner service.

LITERATURE
Howard, *Chinese Armorial Porcelain*, p. 406; the earlier dinner service, p. 582.

## 164
## Teapot

Qianlong, c.1770
Height: 5¾ in (14.7 cm)

Of inverted pear shape with vertical moulding, barbed spout and shaped handle; the cover moulded to match, with peach finial. On either side a large circular panel with a Chinese merchant seated on a river terrace, while a girl stands beside him holding a fan.

This shape owes its origin to a more delicate and simple Meissen form but the piece lacks its charm, and the decoration is mechanical. The simple globular teapots which had dominated the market until the 1760s gave way to these clumsier and larger forms for more than a decade, before copying the silver-inspired drum shapes that followed in the last two decades of the 18th century and much of the 19th.

## 166
## Teapot

Qianlong, c.1790
Height: 4½ in (11.5 cm)

Of simple drum shape after silver,
the cover with strawberry finial,
and the crossed strap handles joining
the body amongst vine clusters. The
top and cover with bands of
underglaze blue trellis, and an
enamelled shield with initials 'JEA'
on either side beneath mantling and
a knotted bow.

At this time, this was the standard
teapot for special orders with
initials. The porcelain came in
quantity from Jingdezhen via
Nanking and thence by sea, and was
enamelled with standardized shields
in the workshops of Canton, where
initials could be added quickly so
that orders could return on the ships
that brought them. Supercargoes
would fulfil commissions for tea
services from private clients and
European and American china
shops. The services bought by
George Washington, Sir Joshua
Reynolds and many others in the
late 1780s and 1790s had teapots of
this shape, although often with
differing underglaze blue
decoration.

## 167
## Coffee Pot

Kangxi, c.1700
Height: $11\frac{1}{4}$ in (28.6 cm)

Of tapering octagonal form and
standing on three spherical feet with
straight spout and S-shaped brace,
long looped handle with tail, and
domed cover with lion finial.
Decorated solely in underglaze blue,
the lower half with scenes after
delftware, and above with scrolls
and diapers and two panels
depicting Europa and the Bull. A
long silver chain attaches the cover
to the handle.

The form is based on silverware,
but the decoration derives from
Delft pottery with scenes of hunting
and foraging, with European
buildings among trees behind.

LITERATURE
Howard & Ayers, *China for the
West*, pp. 74–5 where a restored
example, formerly in the Ionides
Collection, is illustrated.

## 168
## Coffee Pot

Yongzheng, c.1735
Height: 8¾ in (22.4 cm)

Of plain conical shape with high domed cover and bud finial, the long tapering octagonal spout and strap handle at right angles. The floral decoration in underglaze blue with iron-red added, and bands of blue trellis at lip and on cover.

This form closely follows the shape of silver coffee pots popular in England. The decoration shows every sign of having been first designed in underglaze blue only, but with red added in China (probably to improve sales). Such a pot may well have been chosen by a supercargo in a Canton shop, for it is unlikely that it would have been included in larger orders for underglaze blue or Chinese Imari porcelain.

LITERATURE
Sotheby's, *Chinese Export Porcelain Catalogue*, 11 May 1993, Lot 24, which illustrates a blue and white coffee pot of exactly this design and size *without* the additional red decoration.

## 169
## Coffee Pot

Yongzheng, c.1735
Height: 6¾ in (17.2 cm)

Of cylindrical form with ostrich head spout and ostrich tail handle, the high concave domed cover with pointed baluster finial. The body decorated with four alternating ovals, two of European figures and two floral, between five border designs above and five below. The cover with four *rose-verte* lappets and the ostrich spout and handle decorated in realistic strokes of iron-red.

This most unusual coffee pot has all the appearance of a novelty created in the form of a mug and cover, with bird-like spout and handle mimicking a fashion just gaining popularity in Europe.

It was clearly specially commissioned and although apparently for western use, it could have been regarded by a Chinese buyer as an interesting western novelty.

## 170
# Coffee Pot
Yongzheng, c.1735
Height: 13 in (33 cm)

Of pear shape with domed cover and large seated Buddhistic lion finial; the long slender handle and spout (with S-shaped bracket) both emerging from gilt dragons' mouths. Heavily decorated with a diaper band around the lip and on the cover; painted on either side, within scrolling flowers and tendrils, with European gentlemen and ladies and a boy servant.

Although the size is large for a coffee pot, this seems the most likely use for a pot with such a spout; a smaller ($7\frac{1}{2}$ in or 19 cm) version of the same form and decoration is in the Chinese Pavilion in Brussels (with a dragon mask on the spout – not present in this example).

This is one of only a small number made and certainly specially commissioned (see also the unusual cylindrical coffee pot of this type, no. 169).

LITERATURE
Hervouët & Bruneau, *La Porcelaine des Compagnies des Indes à Décor Occidental*, p. 68, Brussels coffee pot. Jörg, *Chinese Export Porcelain . . . Royal Museums, Brussels*, p. 110 for a very similar pot dated ten years earlier.

## 171
## Coffee Pot

Qianlong, c.1740
Height: 12¼ in (30.9 cm)

Of tall conical shape with high domed pointed cover and bud finial above a collar, the tapering octagonal spout and strap handle at right angles. The decoration, specially designed in Europe, of turquoise green scales divided by a broad white area decorated with butterflies and insects above a shaped black band with *famille rose* flowers. The handle heavily enamelled in black, with gold decoration and similar bands of black at the lip, round the finial and at the spout.

Although the pot is very similar in shape to no. 168, the most unusual design was clearly the work of the studio of Cornelis Pronk (see nos 53–7). The scales and colouring appear on a number of other Pronk designs, and the handle is like that of the 'Trumpeter' service (no. 202), while similar butterflies and insects surround the 'Arbour' design (nos 55, 56).

This coffee pot is most unusual (one hesitates to say unique) and may have been privately commissioned as part of a single service.

LITERATURE
Jörg, *Pronk Porcelain*, pp. 77–81 for similar elements of design.

## 172
## Coffee Pot

Qianlong, c.1750
Height: 9 in (23 cm)

Of pear shape with high domed cover and peach finial, shaped ribbed handle and protruding moulded spout. Decorated at the lip and on the cover with European gilt scrollwork, and on each side with an armorial on a diamond-shaped shield beneath a coronet.

This form of coffee pot derives from Meissen porcelain of about 1740 and the gold decoration is in keeping. The arms are of a lady and probably of Asserac of Brittany (although the English family of Bassingbourn has the same shield, the coronet is inappropriate).

## 173
## Coffee Pot

Qianlong, c.1750
Height: 6¾ in (16.2 cm)

Of octagonal oval section and
originally derived from a northern
European silver form, the handle in
imitation of wood attached by silver
brackets. The narrower facets with
Meissen-style scrollwork with
figures, and on either side armorials
and initials.

The arms are accolé, with
supporters which represent the sea
and possibly the wind. The cypher
is 'G' and the arms are of
Gripenberg of Sweden.

REFERENCE
A shaped oval dish of the matching
dinner service is in the Gothenburg
Historical Museum, Inv. no. 19.130.

## 174
## Coffee Pot

Qianlong, c.1795
Height: 8 in (20.3 cm)

Of cylindrical form, with rococo
spout and pistol grip handle set at
right angles; the cover with
strawberry finial. Very simply
decorated with wavy dark blue
enamel lines, and a shield within
mantling with initials 'GB'.

This was one of two popular forms
of coffee pot in the last decade of
the 18th century, based on a
European silver form with wooden
handle (the other form being
conical).

The undecorated ware was
delivered in quantity to Canton
from Jingdezhen and completed to
special European order with initials
only, or initials and crest, as part of
commissioned coffee or tea services.

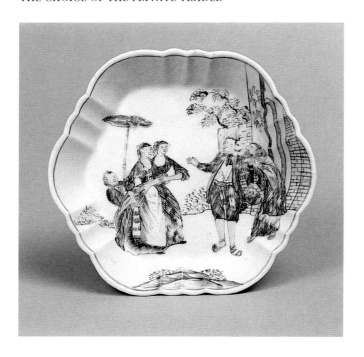

## 176
## Tea or Coffee Pot Stand

Qianlong, c.1780
Width: 6½ in (16.6 cm)

Of very white porcelain in an eight-lobed oval form, decorated on the rim with gold, and with an armorial in *famille rose* and silver enamel between four sprays of European-style flowers.

This tea or coffee pot stand was designed for small bullet-shaped teapots and pear-shaped coffee pots, as made at Meissen. (The drum teapot with these arms, no. 165, does not fit on such a stand.) The arms are of Frederick Ginkel, 5th Earl of Athlone.

## 175
## Teapot Stand

Qianlong, c.1750
Width: 5 in (12.8 cm)

Of fluted hexagonal shape and decorated *en grisaille* with an old and a young man meeting two girls in a street while their servant holds a parasol. The faces and hands tinted pink.

The scene is after a popular European engraving by Lancret, '*Les Oies de Frère Philippe*' (The Geese of Brother Philip) and was copied on Chinese porcelain between 1745 and 1755 with at least four different borders. It tells the story from Boccaccio's *Decameron* of the inexperienced young countryman who is attracted to two girls on his first visit to Florence, and is told by his father that 'they are evil . . . and are called goslings.'

LITERATURE
Scheurleer, *Chinese Export Porcelain*, pls 217, 218 where the original engraving and the scene within a floral border are illustrated. Howard & Ayers, *China for the West*, pp. 346–7, where the story from the *Decameron* is told in greater detail.

## 177
## Spoon Tray

Qianlong, c.1740
Length: 4¾ in (12.3 cm)

Of fluted oblong hexagonal shape, decorated in a panel within gilt scrollwork with three men looking at a woman, while a servant boy pours water from a jug.

This scene is copied in reverse (and without much understanding) from an engraving by Thomassin entitled 'The Coquette meeting her Admirers' and shows the lady on the left with a young, an old and a middle-aged man. In this instance, the scene may be copied from a Meissen example of about 1735.

The spoon tray was an essential part of early tea services, for a hostess offered only one teaspoon on a spoon tray and guests stirred in turn as they took their sugar. About 1750 it became fashionable to make sets of teaspoons, and thereafter spoon trays gradually became unnecessary, although they continued to be made in China until the end of the 18th century.

LITERATURE
Ducret, *Meissner Porzellan* (1972), vol. II, fig. 196, a Meissen example. Scheurleer, *Chinese Export Porcelain*, figs 219, 221 where the original engraving is illustrated.

## 178
## Spoon Tray

Qianlong, c.1795
Length: $4\frac{3}{4}$ in (12.3 cm)

Of lobed hexagonal shape with blue enamelled band and blue and gold spearhead enclosing an armorial with crest.

The arms are of Burton of Derby and, according to legend, granted by King Richard 'Coeur de Lion' to James de Burton who was his esquire in the First Crusade. A descendant was Sir William Burton, Standard-Bearer to Henry VI.

By 1795 spoon trays were not a necessary part of a tea set but often continued to be made in China, though not in England.

LITERATURE
Howard, *Chinese Armorial Porcelain*, p. 984.

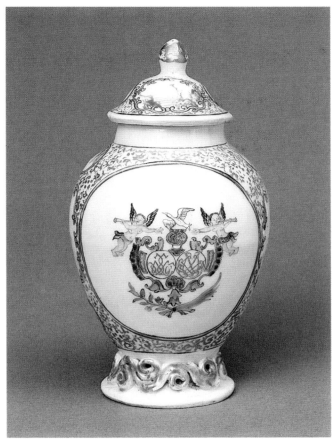

## 179
## Teapoy

Yongzheng, c.1730
Height: $4\frac{1}{2}$ in (11.6 cm)

Of rectangular section with slightly
canted corners and a circular cover;
decorated all over with pink and
black honeycomb diaper within
bands of heavy gilt scrollwork, and
with stylized crimson-and-gold
flowers. On each longer side a boar
crest.

The teapoy or tea caddy was an
essential part of tea 'equipage' for it
contained the tea leaves which were
added to the pot by the hostess at
table. Most services had two
teapoys for different qualities of tea.
The square and rectangular shapes
were popular until about 1735.

This service bears the crest of both
Grice and Harper, but the service
was made for the Grice family as
revealed on some larger pieces of
the service that have the full arms.
The Grice family came from
Brokedish in Norfolk.

LITERATURE
Howard, *Chinese Armorial Porcelain*,
p. 994, incorrectly attributed to
Harper.

## 180
## Teapoy

Qianlong, c.1750
Height: $5\frac{3}{8}$ in (13.7 cm)

Of ovoid shape with applied
scrollwork at the foot; decorated
heavily with gold scrollwork over
much of the body and cover, with
reserves painted *en camaieu*. On one
side a marriage device of two ovals
with cyphers, beneath a helmet and
dove crest held by two angels.

This shape of teapoy was most
common from 1735 to about 1765.
This example has a pseudo armorial
(the crest more likely signifying
marital bliss than of any heraldic
significance).

## 181
## Teapoy

Qianlong, c.1755
Height: 5½ in (14 cm)

Of rectangular form with arched shoulders with overhanging rim, the cover slightly domed with strawberry finial. The shoulders and cover with gilt Meissen-style decoration and both faces with a large armorial.

This teapoy is an early example of the principal form of teapoy made in the second half of the 18th century. The service included two of this shape, and one ovoid of earlier date with scrolling at the foot with the same Meissen decoration and armorial. This must lead to speculation that the former were replacements, for no other service is recorded with two shapes of teapoy.

The tea set and dinner service with these arms (part of which remains with the family) was made about 1745 and descended to the Steward family of Dorset.

LITERATURE
Howard, *Chinese Armorial Porcelain*, p. 309.

## 182
### Teapoy
Qianlong, c.1780
Height: 6 in (15.2 cm)

Of ovoid shape with gently moulded vertical ribbing on the body, decorated with three highly coloured mythical birds beneath gilt swags and a band of green and gold husks. The cover with flat topped finial.

The Chinese ovoid teapoy with applied scrolling foot had given way to the arched teapoy after about 1765, but various European factories, particularly Meissen, had adopted the earlier Chinese form, usually without the scroll at the foot.

The use of fabulous birds at Meissen, Chelsea, Worcester and other factories was in vogue, and in this case the Chinese have copied one of these for a special order.

LITERATURE
Howard & Ayers, *China for the West*, p. 554 where a tureen is decorated in similar manner, and p. 424 where plates have birds of the same type (together with a Meissen coffee pot so decorated).

## 183
### Milk Jug
Kangxi, c.1710
Height: $5\frac{1}{8}$ in (13 cm)

Of pear-shaped form; decorated in underglaze blue with Chinese ladies and a child playing in a garden, beneath a trellis band at the lip which has a jutting spout. The cover and handle fitted in an early 18th-century silver mount with hinge and shell-shaped thumb piece, the handle with turned up end.

It is doubtful that this sophisticated milk jug belonged to a tea or coffee set, but it may have been part of a general order which was mounted with silver shortly after arrival in Europe, probably in Amsterdam. The handle has the same type of ending as similar vessels in the Vung Tau underwater cargo of c.1695.

This jug was probably used for hot milk, but possibly also for chocolate.

## 184
## Milk Jug

Qianlong, c.1735
Height: 4½ in (11.5 cm)

Of pear shape with long curving spout and high curved handle, the body and cover with applied moulded lotus stems and leaves, and painted with carp swimming among aquatic plants in rich *famille rose*.

For up to a decade from 1730 to 1740 some teapots, milk jugs and cups and saucers were decorated with applied stems and flowers – often forming loops under the base. It must have been an expensive addition to the already well decorated pieces, but was the fashion.

This piece is probably a hot-milk jug (although it could be from a condiment set) and would have been part of a set purchased privately from a Canton merchant.

## 185
## Milk Jug

Qianlong, c.1745
Height: 4½ in (11.5 cm)

Of squat pear-shaped form, decorated in natural colours with a young man and woman in a woodland glade – he dressed in a yellow plaid with horn at his waist, and she holding a tablet (possibly an embroidery?) which he is studying – a dalmatian hound at his feet. The rim with simple double line.

This romantic scene is very similar to others on Chinese porcelain where the figures have been identified as Cupid and Psyche (or Venus and Adonis), but this is much more likely to be a rural idyll in semi-classical form. The shepherd, for so his horn proclaims him, has a spear but is much more intent on reading the tablet, perhaps a love letter. Behind the girl is a wicker cage with two doves – emblematic of 'the tender trap'.

LITERATURE
Howard & Ayers, *China for the West*, p. 330, a cup and saucer with the same scene and 'Cupid and Psyche' on a similar jug.

## 186
## Milk Jug

Qianlong, c.1770
Height: 5¾ in (14.6 cm)

Of oval section rising on a fluted pedestal from a round base, and with outward-turned and flaring rim and spout; the handle in simulated bamboo form. Painted with an elephant facing a tree.

This type of milk jug does not appear to develop from a European form but became increasingly popular after about 1770 – and indeed was the principal form of Chinese milk jug until well into the 19th century. Among its advantages is that it did not have a cover, and this must have saved a great deal of trouble to merchants in matching batches of jugs and covers (the evidence of recent underwater cargoes is that large numbers of lids were often packed together for bulk orders and fitted to individual teapots or milk jugs on arrival in Europe).

Although the decoration is an elephant, this jug is likely to have been made for the European market as part of a private order.

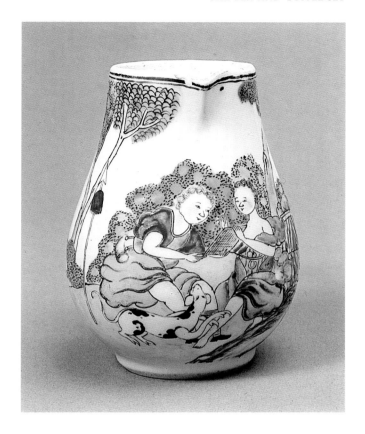

## 187
## Pair of Jugs

Qianlong, c.1775
Height: 7 in (17.8 cm)

Of pear shape with simple protruding spout, and flat covers with urn-type finials, the handles of ogee shape. The flowers are European though of uncertain species.

These jugs are copied from a western model – probably northern European – and must have been specially commissioned. Their use is not established, although it was possibly for hot milk or chocolate.

## 188
## Milk Jug

Qianlong, c.1790
Height: $5\frac{1}{4}$ in (13.4 cm)

Of simple pear shape with slightly domed cover and strawberry finial, the crossed ribbed handles joined to the body with vine leaves and grapes. Decorated with a band of finely drawn gilt trellis at the rim lined with bright pale-green lappets, the body with an armorial between two small flower sprays.

This shape was the most popular form of milk jug and cover during the last three decades of the 18th century. Although they were often known as 'hot-milk jugs' (presumably because of their covers) no service is recorded which has both this shape and the helmet shape above for hot and cold milk.

The arms are of Abel Chapman of Highbury Park, the managing owner of four ships at Canton between 1786 and 1802 (and a descendant of Sir John Chapman, Lord Mayor of London in 1688) who married a Miss Bell of Essex and died in 1824.

LITERATURE
Howard, *Chinese Armorial Porcelain*, p. 707.

## 189
## Two Bowls

Yongzheng, c.1735
Width of each: 4⅝ in (11.9 cm)

Two bowls of identical size and form, and both, most unusually, with a six-character Yongzheng mark on the base in underglaze blue within a double ring. One decorated in looped panels of violet honeycomb diaper, yellow trellis and blue Y-diaper, with inside, a spray of peony and finger citron. The other decorated with a lakeside scene in *famille verte* enamels with a black-and-gold scroll rim.

Following the 1682 edict of the Emperor Kangxi that no porcelain for export should be decorated with the mark of a reigning emperor, it is most unusual that these two examples should be so marked.

While other pieces of the service with the 'diaper' bowl are not known, the scenic bowl was part of a tea service of which this was the only piece so marked. It may be more than a coincidence that the covered sugar bowl (both these examples have lost their covers) is the only piece in a European tea service that could be mistaken for a Chinese form. It is possible that the reign mark was painted without the realization that these pieces were for export.

LITERATURE
Howard & Ayers, *China for the West*, p. 161 where the 'diaper' example is illustrated. Formerly in the Martin Hurst Collection.

## 191
## Sugar Bowl

Qianlong, c.1770
Width: 4½ in (11.6 cm)

Of cylindrical form rising from a narrow base with fox-like handles, the domed cover with peach finial. The handles and finial gilded, and the sides with flower sprays about an armorial.

This is an unusual shape of sugar bowl, with the arms of Clavering impaling Palmer, and was made for George Clavering of Axwell Park who married Anna-Maria, widow of Sir John Pale Bt who died in 1766, and daughter of the Revd William Palmer.

The beetle-like charges on the Palmer shield are an excellent example of heraldry's love of puns – used as an aid to remembering armorials – for they are in fact 'palmer's scrips', the small purses with toggles carried by pilgrims. The Chinese painters would certainly have been mystified, but copied a drawing.

LITERATURE
Howard, *Chinese Armorial Porcelain*, p. 469.

## 190
## Sugar Bowl

Qianlong, c.1750
Width: 5¾ in (14.7 cm)

Of ogee form, with indented handles and wide domed cover with spherical finial; decorated round the body with a gilt scroll and shell pattern, the cover with eight small named armorials in *famille rose* about a central shield and crest.

With the history of a plate of this service already given (see no. 81), it is only necessary to mention that the arms are of Theodorus van Reverhorst, a member of the Court of Justice in Batavia.

Handles for sugar bowls appear to have developed in the 1740s for purely practical reasons, so that guests could more easily help themselves to sugar from their hostess's tray.

LITERATURE
Le Corbeiller, *Patterns of Exchange*, p. 99 for the pair to this piece.

## 192
## Sugar Bowl

Qianlong, c.1795
Height: 5¾ in (14.7 cm)

With vertical ribbing on a pedestal foot, crossed strap handles, and domed cover with a strawberry finial. The decoration in blue enamel and gold with initials, probably 'MTN', within an enamelled and gilded roundel.

From about 1775 this was by far the most popular shape of sugar bowl, and the shape retained favour through much of the 19th century although with ever flatter and more angular handles, and the strawberry finial also increasingly flattened.

With almost all export decorating done at Canton by this date, it is clear that initials could be added quickly in gold to services already prepared, so that they could sail on the ship that brought the order. The interpretation of flowery script letters often makes it difficult to be certain of initials.

## 194
## Covered Beaker

Kangxi, c.1695
Height: 4 in (10.3 cm)

Finely potted and flaring from a circular base, the overhanging slightly domed cover with pointed finial. Decorated in underglaze blue with eight petal-topped panels with flowers on tall stems. The glaze slightly rubbed.

The cargo salvaged off the Vung Tau Peninsula and sold in Amsterdam in 1992 contained about 120 such beakers in two main patterns, with as many saucers. Whether such beakers were intended primarily for drinking tea or chocolate is not clear.

LITERATURE
Christie's Amsterdam, catalogue, 7–8 April 1992, Lots 828–38 where another pattern of panels of hatched wisteria and pine is illustrated.

## 193
## Three Wine or Tea Bowls

Chongzhen, c.1640
Diameter: $3\frac{1}{2}$ in (9 cm)

Of simple flaring form and decorated in underglaze blue with orchids and insects; the base with a Chenghua six-character mark. The glaze dull.

These bowls were part of a group of fifty sold in Amsterdam in March 1984 from a cargo salvaged from the South China Seas by Captain Michael Hatcher.

This cargo was on a Chinese vessel approaching Batavia, and it is probable that some bowls were destined for Dutch ships bound for Amsterdam where they would have been auctioned and used (if at all) as teabowls. In Batavia they would probably have been used for rice wine.

LITERATURE
Christie's Amsterdam, catalogue, 14 March 1984, Lots 386–9.

## 195
## Beaker Lid

Kangxi, c.1695
Width: 3½ in (8.8 cm)

Circular, and only slightly domed
without finial, painted in underglaze
blue with a central scene of a king
and queen seated beneath an awning
on a terrace, surrounded by ten
alternate panels of kneeling figures
and small sprays of flowers. The
glaze worn.

This beaker lid was one of about
thirty from the Vung Tau cargo,
auctioned in Amsterdam in 1992.
No beakers of this pattern were
recovered. It is not clear whether
these were spare lids or whether the
beakers were lost.

The scene is first recorded as
illustrated on porcelain in
Jacquemart & LeBlant's book of
1862, which shows a beaker (the
shape as no. 194) and a cover. On
the beaker the kneeling figure is
before the monarch, and round the
rim is inscribed 'L'EMPIRE DE LA
VERTU, EST ETABLY JUSQU'AU BOUT
DE L'UNIVERS'. It shows Queen
Blanche of France, about 1230,
telling her son Louis IX (known as
'the Saint'): 'The Empire of virtue
stretches to the ends of the World.'

It has been suggested that these cups
were commissioned to remind
Louis IX's descendant, Louis XIV,
who ruled almost five centuries
later, of the importance of virtue. If
so, they were not a conspicuous
success.

LITERATURE
Jacquemart & LeBlant, *Histoire de la
Porcelaine*, pl. XVI.

## 196
## Teabowl and Saucer

Kangxi, c.1722
Diameter of saucer: $3\frac{1}{2}$ in (9 cm)

Decorated with *rouge-de-fer* and gold band at rim, enclosing *famille verte* sprays of pomegranates and flowers, and large central armorial on the saucer in underglaze blue and *famille verte* enamels. The small teabowl with crest only.

The arms are of Woodford impaling Lear, and a Mr M. Woodford is recorded sailing on the *Wyndham* in Canton in 1733 – although it is possible this service was made for another member of the family. The family was connected with the East India Company and had three services with these arms between 1720 and 1730.

LITERATURE
Howard, *Chinese Armorial Porcelain*, pp. 196–7, 995 where the three different services are illustrated.

## 197
## Teabowl and Saucer

Yongzheng, c.1730
Diameter of saucer: 4¾ in (11 cm)

Of circular form with deep straight sides, decorated with a central cockerel, and radiating fan-like designs in gold and rose diaper with *famille rose* flowers on the rim on a gilt background.

Among the birds painted on Chinese Export porcelain, the cockerel and the heron were perhaps the most popular.

LITERATURE
Howard & Ayers, *China for the West*, p. 164.

## 198
## Teabowl and Saucer

Yongzheng, c.1730
Diameter of saucer: 4¼ in (10.8 cm)

Of fluted form with multi-segmented and scalloped rim, each panel decorated with one of four different diapers, enclosing a scene of two fishermen hauling nets. At this time, fishermen and horsemen appear to have been the most popular male figures depicted. They represented recognizable classes in a romantic vision of 'Cathay'. It was essential to the importers of porcelain that their tea wares should please the comfortable ladies of 18th-century Europe by presenting an oriental type of rural idyll.

PROVENANCE
Martin Hurst and Mottahedeh Collections.

LITERATURE
Howard & Ayers, *China for the West*, pp. 156–7.

## 199
## Saucer

Yongzheng, c.1730
Diameter: $4\frac{1}{2}$ in (11.6 cm)

Intricately decorated with a lakeside scene with jetties and small trading boats in an irregular cartouche within Y-diaper in turquoise blue.

This saucer is from a tea service of which a variety with slightly differing scenes were painted in the 1730s. The only European-inspired decoration on such tea wares at this time was armorial, but there was an insatiable demand in Europe for a glimpse of China, and the spectacular (and often idealized) scenery was much sought after.

There was considerable choice of tea 'equipage' from Chinese merchants in Canton, and scenes of this quality were probably not made to any special order. They represent almost the last examples of high quality Chinese taste in the Export porcelain market before it was flooded with European designs and ideas.

THE TEA AND COFFEE SET

## 200
## Coffee Cup and Saucer

Yongzheng, c.1735
Diameter of saucer: 4½ in (11.6 cm)

Painted largely in *famille verte* enamels with the addition of black and gold, with a lakeside scene within a simple black border with gold scrollwork.

It is of considerable interest that the sugar bowl of this service (no. 189) is one of a small number of pieces in Export porcelain with a Yongzheng mark in underglaze blue. The quality of brushwork, however, is not of the same quality as on the other services shown on this page.

The tea and coffee service (dinner plates with this design are not recorded) would have been one of many available in Canton for East India merchants and supercargoes.

## 201
## Coffee Cup and Saucer

Yongzheng, c.1735
Diameter of saucer: 4½ in (11.6 cm)

Finely painted with a mountainous lakeside scene *en camaieu* within an irregular band of red and gold, and three larger and three small shaped panels with similar lakeside scenes and gold scrollwork. The coffee cup with simple, almost ungainly handle.

It is clear that the demand for very high quality tea and coffee services with Chinese scenes remained particularly strong throughout the 1730s.

## 202
## Coffee Cup and Two Saucers

Qianlong, c.1740
Diameter of saucers: $4\frac{1}{2}$ in and $4\frac{5}{8}$ in ($11.4$ cm and $11.8$ cm)

Decorated with two figures in Ottoman costume in turquoise and yellow playing a trumpet and a French horn, on a heavy black enamel background with gilt spearhead design at rim. The cup and one saucer with a gilt patterned band outside the spearhead. The design is often known as 'Trumpeter'.

There is little doubt that this proved an expensive design to paint, and the cup and saucer on the right are probably from the first order while the other, more simply decorated saucer is from a repeat order when greater attention was being paid to cost.

The design is clearly European in origin, but whether from the studio of Cornelis Pronk is impossible to say. The European style of cup handle may illustrate a porcelain original. It would seem that the more elaborate design also had the thicker black enamel.

LITERATURE
Scheurleer, *Chinese Export Porcelain*, fig. 92, a milk jug (earlier service). Howard & Ayers, *China for the West*, p. 305, bowl (later service).

## 203
## Teabowl and Saucer

Qianlong, c.1740
Diameter of saucer: $4\frac{1}{2}$ in ($11.4$ cm)

Of simple form, but decorated in a very carefully designed European way, in *famille rose* enamels with a gentleman playing the flute to his lady on swinging chairs with a parrot between them.

The same design is seen on plates with *bianco-sopra-bianco* border and scenic reserves *en camaieu*, and this type of design was developed exclusively for porcelain in the way that Pronk had worked in the previous decade. There is a strong Meissen influence, although no exact European original appears to be recorded.

LITERATURE
Scheurleer, *Chinese Export Porcelain*, pl. E, p. 80 where a plate is illustrated.

## 204
## Teabowl and Saucer

Qianlong, c.1740
Diameter of saucer: 2¾ in (7 cm)

Finely potted and of hexagonal shape with indented corners. A lady with a parasol shows her son three strutting birds.

This is clearly a Chinese version of Pronk's design of the 'Lady with a parasol'. It is painted in the *famille verte* palette which is unusual for this date, and the servant who holds the parasol in Pronk's own version is replaced by a boy for whom the parasol is held.

It would be tempting to speculate that this version preceded Pronk, but the choice of European birds includes a ruff and a spoonbill which are native to Holland.

The obvious popularity of the design, coupled with the cost of the intricate diaper on the original pattern, must have made these simpler copies an attractive alternative. In fact these are rarer than Pronk's own design.

LITERATURE
Jörg, *Pronk Porcelain*, p. 73, IV.

## 205
## Teabowl and Saucer

Qianlong, c.1745
Diameter of saucer: 4¾ in (12.3 cm)

Of fluted circular form, decorated in *famille rose* after a European original, with Paris choosing the most beautiful of three goddesses. There is no border design.

King Priam's son Paris was asked to settle the difficult question of which of the three, Aphrodite, Hera and Athene, was the most beautiful. He is seen handing his apple to Aphrodite, while Cupid seems intent on getting a better view.

This was perhaps the most popular European design on Chinese porcelain during the 1740s, and there are at least six different borders or variations of the scene which allowed the innocent painting of beautiful naked ladies. It is clear from the variation of painting and background that the porcelain was available from a number of different workshops between about 1740 and 1755.

LITERATURE
Scheurleer, *Chinese Export Porcelain*, illus. 225, 226.
Beurdeley, *Porcelain of the East India Company*, Cat. 31, 130.
Howard & Ayers, *China for the West*, p. 329.

## 206
## Teabowl and Saucer

Qianlong, c.1745
Diameter of saucer: 4¾ in (12 cm)

Painted only *en grisaille*, after an untraced European engraving with a half-naked girl attracting the unwelcome attention of two elderly men. The border of feathery scrollwork.

The story of the unfortunate Susannah, who killed herself after feeling great guilt when she attracted the advances of two Jewish Elders, is well known.

It is much more likely that the porcelain was painted with this scene because it provided an opportunity to show an erotic moment than for any religious reason. Clearly a small number of pieces of this rare Export porcelain were commissioned by a merchant. It was possibly an order not repeated.

## 207
## Teabowl and Saucer

Qianlong, c.1750
Diameter of saucer: $5\frac{1}{4}$ in (13.5 cm)

Decorated in underglaze blue
without gilding, with a simple
lakeside scene with small pavilions
on promontories. The outside of
cup and reverse rim of saucer with a
rich brown glaze.

Illustrating the simplest form of
'lakeside scene' about two decades
after the finely painted examples
nos 199–201, this ware was known
as 'Batavia Ware' (after its
popularity in that city). The
example is from the cargo of the
*Geldermalsen*, which sank in January
1752 and was salvaged by Captain
Hatcher.

Such teabowls and saucers were not
specially commissioned, as was
evident from the manifest and
packing of the *Geldermalsen* cargo.

LITERATURE
Christie's Amsterdam, catalogue, 28
April–2 May 1986, Lots 5600–38;
1,674 such cups and saucers were
sold called 'Batavian Pavilion' at the
auction.

## 209
## Cup and Saucer

Qianlong, c.1755
Diameter of saucer: $4\frac{5}{8}$ in (11.8 cm)

Decorated in *famille rose* after a European engraving with three putti on rockwork blowing bubbles, and before them a stone pyramid, a wicker cage and various discarded instruments – coronet, drumsticks and palette – in a rock garden landscape, with the mask of a man lying in the foreground. The border with loose scrollwork entwined with leaves.

Such a design, clearly sent from Europe, needs to be understood before it can be interpreted, but possibly represents a collage of masonry (the pyramid and suns in border) and the arts – palette and actor's mask. The intended market is unclear, but the border suggests a Continental rather than British origin.

Very few examples are known and possibly only one service was made.

LITERATURE
Hervouët & Bruneau, *La Porcelaine des Compagnies des Indes*, p. 321 where a plate and saucer are illustrated and it is suggested the design is in the manner of a series of engravings by N. Cochin fils in *Science et Géométrie*.

## 208
## Tea Beaker and Saucer

Qianlong, c.1755
Diameter of saucer: $4\frac{1}{2}$ in (11.4 cm)

Constructed in two layers, the outer layer of the cup and upper layer of the saucer pierced in a floral pattern and gilded and enamelled. In the centre of the saucer a spray of predominantly Chinese flowers.

Although the Chinese were adept at creating double-layered, pierced porcelain for decorative reasons, it seems more likely in this case that it was done for practical reasons, so that a user could hold a cup that contained a very hot beverage.

The obvious disadvantage was cost and difficulty of cleaning. Relatively few such cups and saucers survive in Europe.

## 210
## Teabowl and Saucer

Qianlong, c.1760
Diameter of saucer: $4\frac{3}{4}$ in (12 cm)

Decorated solely in grey after an engraving, with a portrait surrounded by the legend 'DE EDEIE GROOT ACHTBARE HEER MIS LIEVE GEELVINCR' (in reverse), with an armorial and a European scroll and diaper rim in the manner of du Paquier.

This tea service was copied exactly from a Dutch portrait engraving of 1758 by J. Houbraken after a painting by J. Wandelaar and the inscription translates 'Heer Lieve Geelvinck, Master of Laws'.

Mr Geelvinck was Burgomaster of Amsterdam and an official of the Dutch East India Company. He had earlier had a *famille rose* dinner service with these arms.

LITERATURE
Howard & Ayers, *China for the West*, p. 256.

## 211
## Pair of Two-Handled Cups and Saucers

Qianlong, c.1775
Diameter of saucers: 5½ in (14 cm)

The two-handled cup of beaker form with scalloped rim (as also the saucer). Almost the whole surface is decorated with veined broad leaves in blue, yellow and turquoise, intermingled with flowers.

This pattern was probably derived from Indian textile designs and has become known as 'tobacco leaf' – after the broad leaves which are its principal theme. The design has variations which include birds and figures among the leaves. In the early 19th century a similar design covered the whole surface (see no. 251).

LITERATURE
Howard & Ayers, *China for the West*, pp. 540–3 where five variations are illustrated.

## 212
## Teabowl and Saucer

Qianlong, c.1785
Diameter of saucer: 3½ in (9 cm)

Decorated with small sprays of flowers and a pink scale band at rim; in the centre the crest of an owl over a cypher 'WW'.

The service is finely painted and has the crest and initials of William Woodley, Governor of the Leeward Islands in 1784.

The Woodleys were a Norfolk family and the service was acquired after his death by a Mr Owles of Lowestoft. When it was sold in Lowestoft in October 1872, Mr William Chaffer, the author of *Marks and Monograms on Pottery and Porcelain*, considered it as final proof that such ware was decorated in Lowestoft – sometimes using oriental porcelain. When the site of the Lowestoft factory was found in the early 20th century, the very large number of shards revealed not one piece of Chinese hard-paste porcelain.

In spite of that, the terms 'Oriental Lowestoft' and 'Lowestoft' were commonly used for Chinese Export porcelain until the 1950s – largely on account of Chaffer's incorrect attribution after seeing this service.

LITERATURE
Howard, *Chinese Armorial Porcelain*, pp. 32–34 where the details are given in full.

## 213
## Teabowl and Saucer

Jiaqing, c.1805
Diameter of saucer; $5\frac{1}{2}$ in (14 cm)

Finely decorated in rich blue and rose-pink enamels, with a trellis border punctuated by four well painted scenic panels, and fringed with a classical frieze and butterflies. In the centre a pictorial roundel with two classical figures, perhaps both women, in a European landscape, one kneeling as the other appears to paint (or carve) on a tree.

In spite of the fine painting, it is clear that the Chinese decorators were unsure of the exact meaning of the European engraving they were copying.

The butterflies derive from the Fitzhugh border of the previous decades, and a saucer of similar design with Mount Vernon in the centre, painted in coral and gold, was in the Mottahedeh Collection. This must suggest the possibility that this service also was made primarily for the American market.

LITERATURE
Howard & Ayers, *China for the West*, p. 495, a similar border with Mount Vernon.

# Other Drinking Vessels

## Examples, c.1640–c.1820

Europe had always used a wide variety of materials for drinking vessels, including silver, pewter, leather, horn, pottery and glass.

Efforts made by merchants in the China trade in the 17th and 18th centuries to develop Chinese porcelain as an alternative material (both for drinking and for pouring vessels) met with varying success.

The main rivalry was between porcelain and glass, and while the use of porcelain for hot beverages has now become almost universal, for other uses it was to prove less successful.

Some bottles and jugs were also used for purposes other than drinking, but have been included in this section (with the bowls made to accompany them) for comparison.

## 214
## Two Stem Cups

Chongzhen, c.1640
Height: $1\frac{7}{8}$ in (4.8 cm)

Of simple cup form on a concave conical base, painted in underglaze blue with a dragon chasing a flaming pearl. The glaze slightly worn.

These small stem cups were part of the salvaged cargo of a Chinese trading vessel which sank in the South China Seas shortly after 1643. There is little doubt that the large numbers of small stem cups and wine cups of this size were used in the East for rice wine, while those that reached Europe may have been used for gin. It is likely, however, that much of this supply was used in Batavia itself and only relatively small numbers were selected by the supercargoes for Europe.

LITERATURE
Christie's Amsterdam, catalogue, 14 March 1984, Lots 176 et seq. In the March and June sales about 520 were sold.

## 215
## Goblet

Kangxi, c.1700
Height: 6 in (15.2 cm)

With deep narrow bowl and everted rim, the stem with slight knop and small domed foot with slight fluting; decorated in underglaze blue with sprays of flowers and foliage, and more formal decoration at lip, on the stem and at the foot.

This copies a European wine glass of c.1700, and the comparatively small number of pieces of this shape almost certainly points to the greater popularity of its glass competitor.

A number of similar goblets of more elegant form and decorated with river scenes were in the cargo of a Chinese junk sunk off the Vung Tau Peninusula about 1695. That cargo was composed of larger orders, which Dutch merchants would have consolidated with other supplies for direct shipment from Batavia to Holland.

LITERATURE
Christie's Amsterdam, 7–8 April 1992, Lots 23–28 (13 goblets from the Vung Tau cargo).

## 217
## Monteith

Kangxi, c.1710
Height: 9 in (23 cm)

Of cylindrical form, with flaring foot and shaped rim composed of six triple lobes, and with simple hook-shaped handles. Decorated with figures in pavilions in red, gold and touches of black, with floral borders in the manner of Arita ware.

The heavy potting suggests that this may have been copied from a simplified wooden model of a silver monteith of about 1700–10.

The shape of such pieces was designed to enable glasses to be cooled. The centre of the monteith was filled with crushed ice and the bowls of each glass were laid on this for chilling, while the feet rested outside each cut.

The Chinese were copying silver monteiths which had been used in England since 1683, when this form was first recorded. The name was taken from 'Monsieur Monteigh' (or Monteith) whose unusually cut cloak gave rise to the name and to the couplet:

New things produce new words and so Monteith,
Has by one vessel saved himself from death
       King's *Art of Cookery*, 1707

LITERATURE
Lee, *British Silver Monteiths*, in particular illustrations on pp. 23–4 and 29–47, many dated between 1700 and 1715.
Howard & Ayers, *China for the West*, p. 116, a *famille verte* version.

## 216
## Two Libation Cups

First half of 18th century
Width: 5½ in (14 cm)

Standing on a small oval foot with widely flaring lip and with an ivory glaze, and moulded in high relief – one with a monkey and a dragon and the other with a deer, a crane and a lion on the ribbed body.

As the name suggests, these *blanc-de-Chine* cups were made for ritual drinking, and they were modelled on rhinoceros-horn cups. They were brought to Europe from the late 17th century onwards, and were sometimes mounted there as a basket with an ormolu lip of chased lappets and a swing handle. This shape was early copied by Meissen, and there is little doubt that pieces of this quality were brought in private cargo as novelties.

LITERATURE
Howard & Ayers, *China for the West*, pp. 102–3 where three examples from about 1700 to 1800 are illustrated.

218

## Monteith

Kangxi, c.1715
Diameter: 13 in (32.9 cm)

Of bowl shape with eight semi-circular pieces cut from the rim; decorated in underglaze blue with chrysanthemums and scrollwork left in white, and with eight rectangular reserves decorated with birds and mythical beasts. The rim with a red-brown glaze, the inside decorated with eight Chinese antiques.

Some twenty variations in silver are illustrated in Georgina Lee's *British Silver Monteiths*, although with greater decorative detail and with hinged drop-ring handles.

It is perhaps no coincidence that many earlier silver monteiths of c.1690–1700 had chinoiserie decoration.

LITERATURE
Le Corbeiller, *China Trade Porcelain*, pp. 36–7, illustrating a similar bowl in the Metropolitan Museum.

## 219
## Drinking Vessel

Japanese, c.1660–90
Height: 5⅛ in (13 cm)

Of coarse porcelain, in cylindrical form with rounded bottom, resting on three short cabriole legs on a footring; decorated in red, brown, green, yellow and dull purple with European figures standing about a seated figure with a wine cup.

During the mid-17th century, when supplies of Chinese porcelain were very erratic and scarce because of the chaos caused by the fall of the Ming Dynasty, the Dutch increasingly turned their attention to supplies from Japan.

This drinking vessel, which appears to have no exact Western model but certainly has Western inspiration, may be seen as a very early attempt to supply drinking mugs for the European market.

LITERATURE
Howard & Ayers, *China for the West*, p. 126 where the same vessel is illustrated.

## 220
## Mug with Cover

Kangxi, c.1695
Height: 5¼ in (13.5 cm)

Globular in body with cylindrical upper part and ribbed lip, the handle turning outward at base to form three points, and the cover with small seated dog. The decoration in underglaze blue with sprays of flowers and leaves. The glaze dull.

This form was a popular one for stoneware mugs made in Germany from the early 17th century, and its progress can be traced in China through *blanc-de-Chine* models to blue and white, Chinese Imari, *famille verte* and occasionally *famille rose* versions.

This example was part of the cargo of a Chinese trading vessel which sank off the Vung Tau Peninsula about 1695. Such European shapes would have been sold in Batavia to European merchants.

LITERATURE
Christie's Amsterdam, catalogue, 7–8 April 1992, Lots 248–50: eight mugs in all.

## 221
# Mug

Kangxi, c.1718
Height: 7 in (17.8 cm)

Of straight cylindrical form with circular ribbing at foot and a broad strap handle; the rim decorated in underglaze blue diaper with Chinese Imari flowers on one side, while on the other is an English armorial of late 17th-century form with a baronet's badge.

The arms are of the wealthy East India Company director Sir Gregory Page and his wife, Mary Trotman, whom he married in 1690. He was created a baronet in December 1714, and the dinner service of which this mug forms a part was made between 1715 and his death in 1720. The service and mugs are of exactly the same design as another armorial service made for Sir Gregory's daughter and her husband, who married in 1718.

LITERATURE
Howard, *Chinese Armorial Porcelain*, p. 179, p. 180 for service of Sir Gregory's daughter, Turner impaling Page.

## 222
## Mug

Kangxi, c.1722
Height: 5¾ in (14.7 cm)

Of cylindrical form with circular ribbing at foot and plain handle; richly decorated with a band of *rouge-de-fer* and gold at rim and of spearhead at base enclosing a very large armorial – with traces of *famille rose* enamels. The reverse with *famille verte* flowers.

The large dinner service of which this forms a part was made at the time of the introduction of *famille rose* enamels. The *famille verte* flowers and ribbing are typical of the late Kangxi period which ended in 1722, while the crest, crest cap and motto scroll introduce the new opaque rose enamel.

The arms are of Lord Trevor of Bromham impaling Weldon. Thomas Trevor was Solicitor-General in 1702, and successively

Lord Chief Justice, Lord Privy Seal and Lord President of the Council. He had married secondly in 1700 his cousin Anne Weldon, and died in 1730.

LITERATURE
Howard, *Chinese Armorial Porcelain*, p. 199, where a similar mug is illustrated with a plate of the same design made for Lord Trevor's daughter and son-in-law.

## 223
## Mug

Yongzheng, c.1725
Height: 5¾ in (14.7 cm)

Of rare conical form, with ribs at foot and rim and broad strap handle; painted at the rim with a band of underglaze blue diaper interspersed with chrysanthemum and panels of red stems, and on the body with Chinese Imari decoration.

Such a mug is unusual in shape, although a great many were decorated in Imari palette from about 1710 to 1745. It is undoubtedly copied from a European silver original.

## 224
## Mug

Qianlong, c.1750
Height: 6 in (15.2 cm)

Of bell shape, decorated below the rim with a gilt shell and scroll design, and round the body with a small sailing pinnace with the Union Jack at the bowsprit and similar pennant and flag at the stern, between on either side a cypher 'GW' beneath a mask.

Such bell-shaped mugs were a feature of the 1740s but the style did not long survive after 1750.

The pinnace is rigged with precision, and apparently flies the same flags as one illustrated in a contemporary print entitled 'A View of Virginia River, Chinese Boat etc. in Windsor Great Park' which shows members of the royal family beside their carriages, with the royal coach in the background, watching a small regatta on Virginia Water.

The cypher 'GW' would suggest that the yacht was that of Prince George William Frederick, who later ascended the throne as George III, son of the Prince of Wales (who died in 1751).

LITERATURE
Engraving by R. Hancock, publ. London for Robt. Sayer at the Golden Buck near Serjeants Inn in Fleet Street.

## 225
## Mug

Qianlong, c.1770
Height: 6 in (15.2 cm)

Of barrel shape, with around the rim a band of garden trellis with flowers enclosing a crest, the body with three exotic tropical birds on the grass near garden shrubs of a European nature.

This design derives from a Meissen original of c.1740, and similar, often imaginary, birds were painted on Chinese tea and coffee services at that time. The crest could be of a number of British families including Browne, Bayle, Stephen or Strange, but without a shield it is impossible to say which (see also no. 182 for a later teapoy with similar birds).

LITERATURE
Howard & Ayers, *China for the West*, pp. 424–5 where a plate of the service, another with a different crest, and a Meissen coffee pot are illustrated.

## 226
## Mug

Qianlong, c.1785
Height: 4¼ in (10.7 cm)

Modelled accurately after a Derby original in the form of a bearded face, painted realistically in flesh tints and with blond hair beneath a stylized cap with indented design in orange-red.

The Derby originals usually bear a puce mark of c.1785, and this popular pattern which, with its sailor-like cap, has been called 'Sailor's Head', 'Rodney' or 'Neptune', was made at Chelsea, Derby and other factories – examples of these now being more numerous than the Chinese copies.

Undoubtedly the making of such mugs in China was a purely commercial venture to undercut English prices, but it may be assumed that it was not successful.

LITERATURE
Howard & Ayers, *China for the West*, p. 592 where a Derby example is also illustrated.

## 227
## Mug

Qianlong, c.1795
Height: $5\frac{1}{2}$ in (13.9 cm)

Of cylindrical shape, with cross-strapped handles joining the body with vine leaves and berries, and painted below a blue-enamelled and gold-starred lip with masonic symbols – the Pillars of Solomon's Temple, the seven stars and rain clouds, a level and two plumb lines, the moon, the sun and a compass and book – all in browns and blue.

Such mugs were usually purchased by masons for presentation to their lodges (there are eleven such mugs in Freemasons' Hall in London). The earliest recorded is of c.1750, and masonic porcelain, including punch bowls, was ordered from China until at least 1812.

LITERATURE
Howard & Ayers, *China for the West*, pp. 323–8 where various examples are illustrated (including this mug) and a check list of Chinese masonic porcelain in Freemasons' Hall is given.

## 228
## Set of Mugs

Jiaqing, c.1805
Heights: 6 in, 5½ in and 4¾ in
(15.2 cm, 13.8 cm and 12 cm)

Of cylindrical shape with ribbed and cross-strapped handles with berried ends, decorated below a gilt patterned band with a pastoral scene *en grisaille* of a farmer leaning against a cow. In the background, trees and a high wall or mansion.

A very similar scene, with no buildings, is illustrated on the inside of a bowl at Winterthur, and it is known that similar designs were ordered by Philadelphia Quakers. A dinner service (including mugs) which was made for Isaac and Mary Morris, Quakers of Philadelphia, is said to have been designed by the latter, but is not as well painted as these three mugs and is almost certainly later.

However, an ink-and-wash drawing, probably from Mary

Morris's sketch book, which is exactly as these mugs (and includes the building, although reversed to be behind the cow) is now thought to be after a Dutch engraving. This has an inscription '. . . Pattern for set of China copied by Mary H. Morris Jan 7th 1797' (the date is possibly altered). It must have been a popular design, for there is an invoice dated in Canton as late as 8 January 1816 for 'A teaset of China of 106 (cow landscape)'.

LITERATURE
Mudge, *Chinese Export Porcelain for the American Trade 1785–1835*, first ed. 1962, figs 52–4 illustrate the service.
Palmer, *A Winterthur Guide to Chinese Export Porcelain*, fig. 53 illustrates the bowl.
Jean Gordon Lee, *Philadelphians and the China Trade 1784–1844*, illustrates the actual drawing and provides the details of the last paragraph above.

## 229
## Punch Bowl

Yongzheng, c.1735
Width: 15 in (38 cm)

Very richly decorated in opaque *famille rose* enamels with peonies, chrysanthemum and pheasants beneath an elaborate rim band of sepia scrolling with flowers, and irregular floral panels on sepia whorls and turquoise trellis, with a band inside the rim in the same palette.

The punch bowl occupied an important place in Georgian England, where toasts were drunk and concoctions mixed for gentlemen before and after hunting, and at many social gatherings and dinners.

This example is of the finest quality of its day and would have been ordered privately. Many bowls were parts of sets of three of different sizes, which was convenient for packing.

PROVENANCE
Formerly Martin Hurst Collection.

## 230
## Punch Bowl

Qianlong, c.1750
Width: $10\frac{1}{4}$ in (25.8 cm)

Very finely painted, with an armorial on either side between two large panels decorated with Chinese lakeside villas, small trading vessels and figures on terraces, all surrounded by a gold line entwined with flowers and leaves. Inside with elaborate scrolls, and the chain of an order enclosing a cypher 'G'.

The bowl has the arms of Scotland, with the Order of the Thistle about the arms. A small number of such bowls are known but this is probably the earliest and most elaborate. The cypher is most likely to indicate the Sovereign of the Order, King George II.

This ancient Scottish order was revived by James II in 1687 when eight Scottish noblemen were invested, but because of the confusion caused by the exile of King James two years later it was revived again by Queen Anne in 1703, when the number of knights was increased.

Such a bowl was almost certainly presented to the Order by one of the knights, but there is no record of which.

LITERATURE
Howard, *Chinese Armorial Porcelain*, pp. 504–5 where four different punch bowls, a plate and a mug are illustrated.

## 231
## Punch Bowl

Qianlong, c.1760
Width: $15\frac{1}{2}$ in (39.2 cm)

Decorated in *famille rose* with two scenes after English hunting engravings – one showing huntsmen and hounds searching a cover, and on the reverse a similar scene with the pack and riders. Between these are panels of gilt scrollwork with small vignettes, with inside the rim a spearhead border and a large finger citron.

The painting from which the scene illustrated was engraved is by James Seymour (1702–52) and is entitled 'Beating for a hare'. A number of other engravings after Seymour were used on similar punch bowls, including a set of four fox-hunting scenes engraved by Pierre Canot.

Such bowls were particularly popular for hunt meetings and would have been ordered in Canton by private traders taking sets of engravings to copy.

LITERATURE
Lloyd Hyde, *Oriental Lowestoft*, p. 95 where a similar bowl with this scene is illustrated with the original engraving.
Howard & Ayers, *China for the West*, pp. 281–3 where another set of engravings showing fox-hunting and a bowl are illustrated.

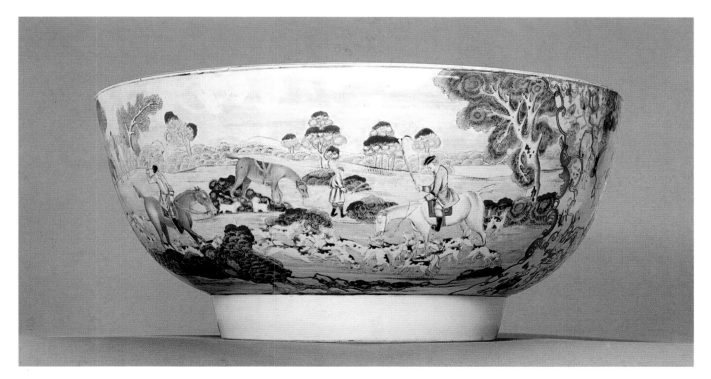

## 232
## Punch Bowl

Qianlong, c.1770
Width: 10 in (25.4 cm)

Painted in *famille rose* enamels with a European man and woman waving farewell to a merchantman under full sail with the flag of the Hon. East India Company.

This scene of 'The Sailor's Farewell', and that of 'The Sailor's Return', were very popular subjects for punch bowls. The ships were usually painted the same but with different flags to suit different markets. The East India Company flag – of red and white stripes with a Union Jack in the upper mast corner – makes it almost certain that this was for the British market.

LITERATURE
Howard & Ayers, *China for the West*, where almost exactly the same design is painted but with a Dutch flag.

## 233
## Punch Bowl

Qianlong, c.1785
Width: $14\frac{1}{4}$ in (36 cm)

Painted with a continuous view of the European factories (or Hongs) at Canton, with the flags of France, Sweden, England and Holland – and a bare pole where the Imperial flag had once flown – showing in the illustration (see chapter 3).

Punch bowls with these flags had been made from about 1764, initially with a view in a single panel, later to be followed by two panels, and from about 1780 with a continuous scene. It was not until about 1788 that the American flag was shown, but in 1785 Captain Green of the *Empress of China* (the first American vessel to trade direct with China) brought back '4 Factory painted @ $5\frac{1}{2}$ each – $22' (the only known recorded invoice for such a bowl).

LITERATURE
Phillips, *China Trade Porcelain*, fig. 8, a bowl of c.1795 with the American flag.
Howard & Ayers, *China for the West*, pp. 208–9, details of a number of bowls.
Howard, *New York & the China Trade*, p. 77, bowl with American flag.

## 234
## Punch Bowl

Qianlong, c.1785
Width: $10\frac{3}{8}$ in (26.2 cm)

Between narrow wavy lines – and
with similar decoration inside – this
bowl is painted twice with two
trade cards. The larger shows a
beaver beneath a tricorn hat, the
card reading 'William Gloster HAT-
MAKER at the Hall and Beaver,
37 Leman Street, Goodman's Fields,
London – Makes fine Beaver and
other Hatts Wholesale & Retail. NB
Hatts turned Dyed Lined & blocked
in the Newest Manner'; below are
two white rabbits and a recumbent
camel.

This is one of very few 'trade'
bowls, which were almost certainly
brought back by friends in the East
India Company. An earlier bowl,
now in an American private
collection, has the sign of a glove
and breeches, and was made about

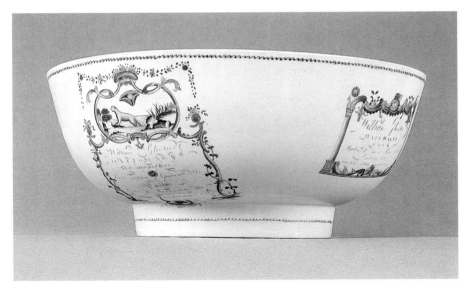

1750. There are mugs of a boat-
builder (at Gravesend), two inn
signs (at Gravesend and
Buckingham) and one of a post
office (at Maidstone, Kent), also a
bowl for a male midwife. In
addition, there were at least twenty-
seven bowls or services made for
livery companies and a number for
societies.

LITERATURE
Howard & Ayers, *China for the
West*, pp. 428–9 where a boat-
builder and post office mug are
illustrated.
Howard, *Chinese Armorial Porcelain*,
pp. 910–11 where a list of City
livery companies with known
services is given.

## 235
## Punch Bowl

Jiaqing, c.1800
Width: $15\frac{1}{4}$ in (38.5 cm)

Decorated below a blue enamel band elaborately gilded with vine leaves with two scenes copied accurately from engravings: one of the Foundling Hospital, with the courtyard filled with carriages and a distant view of St Mary's Islington; the other of the Grand Walk in Vauxhall Gardens, with an orchestra playing music in the Rotunda.

At first sight there seems little to link these views, but the Foundling Hospital (founded by Captain Coram in 1739) was patronized by the aristocracy and by well known philanthropists. Hogarth, Reynolds and William Haydon were among artists who donated their works, and its permanent gallery was influential in leading to the foundation of the Royal Academy. A concert by Handel raised the enormous sum of £7,000 for the Hospital.

Handel was also prominent at

Vauxhall, and Hogarth and later Haydon were involved in the decorations there. Both prints were published in 1750–51, and this punch bowl linked two fashionable London sites.

It can be no coincidence that the size and decoration are exactly as found on another punch bowl of this date in the Mottahedeh Collection – even to identical floral sprays, and with views of the Mansion House and Ironmongers' Hall which are also after engravings of c.1750 – and it seems possible that they were once a pair.

LITERATURE
Christie's London, catalogue, 22 April 1991, where further details are given, and to which the author is indebted for much of the information above.
Howard & Ayers, *China for the West*, pp. 268–9, Mansion House bowl.

ENGRAVINGS
Foundling Hospital, c.1750, for R. Wilkinson of Cornhill.
Vauxhall, c.1750, by John Sebastian Muller after Samuel Wall.

## 236
## Kendi

Chongzhen, c.1640
Height: 8 in (20.5 cm)

Of globular form with tall flaring neck with incurved lip, and bulbous spout; decorated in Kraak manner with panels of flowers and flying horses. The glaze dull.

One of the many forms in the salvaged cargo of c.1643 and as likely to be used in Asia as in Europe. The term *kendi* is Malay, and these drinking vessels, which were sometimes more elaborate with collars at the spout and made in the form of elephant or phoenix, were held by the neck for pouring.

LITERATURE
Scheurleer, *Chinese Export Porcelain*, pls 30, 32, 33 (the latter showing a silver mounted *kendi* of this type in a 17th-century Dutch still-life). Rinaldi, *Kraak Porcelain*, p. 176 where a very similar kendi is illustrated, together with others from c.1590.

## 238
## Apothecary Bottle

Japanese, c.1675
Height: 10 in (25.5 cm)

Of heavy globular form with short neck and two rings at the lip; painted in underglaze blue with a broad band of flowers and birds beneath a geometric design on the shoulder, and on one side the initials 'W:T:R' within a European wreath.

Such bottles were of particular use for medicinal liquids in Europe, but the initials are more likely to indicate the owner than the liquid. The double rings enabled a skin or parchment strip to be tied with a thong over the mouth which could then be sealed with hot wax if the bottle was to be airtight.

LITERATURE
Ford & Impey, *The Gerry Collection at the Metropolitan Museum of Art*, p. 68 where four similar bottles are illustrated.

## 237
## Square Flask

Shunzhi, c.1650
Height: 10¼ in (26.2 cm)

With almost straight sides and shoulder with two slightly raised steps of moulded petals and small cylindrical neck. Painted in underglaze blue with mountain and river scenes in broad washes, the petals also painted and a mask on the neck.

This shape developed from the more rounded 'square' Chinese flasks of the 1630s, and was the forerunner of the square Japanese flask which was available from the 1660s until the early 18th century.

Unlike earthenware, Chinese porcelain was not porous, and such bottles had a number of uses in Europe for spirits and oils.

LITERATURE
Scheurleer, *Chinese Export Porcelain*, fig. 122 (wrongly numbered 121), bottle c.1630.
Ayers, Impey & Mallet, *Porcelain for Palaces*, no. 56 – a Japanese square flask of c.1670.

239
Guglet

Qianlong, c.1745
Height: 10 in (25.5 cm)

Of globular form with long neck and slight knop below a slightly everted lip, painted in *famille rose* enamels with an armorial (and a spray of flowers on the reverse), with two bands of floral chain at the lip.

The name 'guglet' derives from the onomatopaeic 'gug-gug-gug' sound when pouring – in this case almost certainly water. Such guglets were sometimes matched with bowls for washing, but were more usually used at table. The arms are of Flyght impaling Lucas.

LITERATURE
Howard, *Chinese Armorial Porcelain*, p. 608.

## 240

## Guglet and Basin

Qianlong, 1750
Height of bottle: 10 in (25.5 cm)
Width of basin: 10¼ in (26.2 cm)

The bottle of globular form with long neck with knop near the top and flaring lip; the basin with turned-over rim. Both decorated in underglaze blue with a lakeside scene with figures and a hut in the foreground and a pagoda on the further shore. The glaze worn.

Both these pieces, salvaged from the wreck of the *Geldermalsen*, were clearly intended as a set for a washing table. The overhanging lip of the basin was made to fit the cut hole in a washstand. The guglet would have been equally useful as a table flask, but it seems likely that the two were designed to be used together.

LITERATURE
Sheaf & Kilburn, *The Hatcher Porcelain Cargoes*, pp. 140–1.

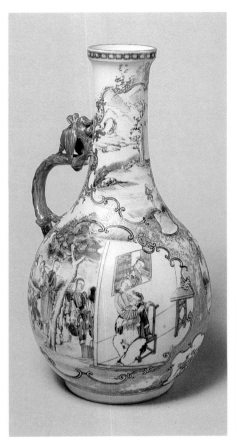

## 241
### Guglet
Qianlong, c.1775
Height: 10½ in (26.8 cm)

Of pear shape with long neck, a raised collar at the rim, and with stylized dragon handle; the decoration with three scenes of Europeans and Chinese in irregular panels within fine gilt scrollwork.

The lower scene illustrated is a remarkably realistic one from what appears to be a 'house of easy virtue', with a European sailor and a Chinese girl in his arms, and other girls outside under the eye of a madam. Vessels with such scenes were almost certainly purchased privately from a china merchant in Canton.

## 242
### Pair of Guglets
French, c.1860
Height: 10 in (25.5 cm)

Of globular form with tall straight necks; decorated in *famille rose* enamels with an armorial between two bands of rose diaper with gilt flowers, and on the neck the crest (intended as 'a thistle erect') above a gilt scrollwork band.

These bottles are painted in exactly the same palette as a Chinese armorial service of c.1730 for the Cruickshank family. They were either replacements or additions, and probably made by Samson of Paris (although other Paris workshops in the mid-19th century made excellent replacements).

What distinguishes Paris replacements from those of English factories is the paste, which is very similar to Chinese but usually whiter, and has led to the assumption that Samson pieces are fakes. This however is only true where *after* completing a family order for replacements, he continued to make further copies, which were sold to shops which labelled them as antique.

LITERATURE
Howard, *Chinese Armorial Porcelain*, p. 239 where a plate of the Chinese service is illustrated.

## 243
## Jug

Chongzhen, c.1640
Height: 9 in (23 cm)

Of pear shape with tall, slightly
flaring neck and sparrow-beak
spout, the handle with high plain
loop. Decorated in underglaze blue
with an official and his servant
meeting a sage on a terrace beneath
formal leafy fronds. A 19th-century
silver cover and hinged mount
attached to the handle.

Such jugs, water bottles and
tankards were ordered in
considerable quantities by the
V.O.C. from 1630 onwards,
although supplies became
increasingly difficult after the death

of Chongzhen in 1644 and the fall
of the Ming Dynasty – and
remained so until after 1660, when
the Qing Dynasty was firmly
established with the reign of the
Emperor Kangxi.

The popularity of these jugs in
Holland in particular is illustrated
by the number now found with
18th- and 19th-century Dutch silver
mounts.

LITERATURE
Scheurleer, *Chinese Export Porcelain*
illustrates a dozen or more vessels of
this period, Cat. 38–53.

## 244
## Pair of Ewers

Kangxi, c.1680
Height: 8 in (20.3 cm)

Of hexagonal vase-shaped section
with slender neck and everted rim
with long lip, standing on a
spreading foot and with very high
looped handle between the shoulder
and rim. Decorated in underglaze
blue with antiques and seated ladies
in fan-shaped panels between
alternate arrangements of lappets
with scrollwork.

Such jugs were probably for the
Portuguese market and certainly
follow a silver form. They were
perhaps used with shaped basins.

LITERATURE
Howard & Ayers, *China for the
West*, p. 81 where a Portuguese
silver example is illustrated with a
silver dish, and a similar Chinese
porcelain basin.

## 245
## Pair of Ewers

Kangxi, c.1710
Height: 11¼ in (28.7 cm)

Of helmet shape, the body with
moulded gadroon at the lip below
which is a mask at the spout, with
petals above the collared stem and
lappets on the foot; the handle with
heavy inward-curling scroll at top.
Decorated in predominantly floral
*famille verte* translucent enamels,
with the bands of gadroon and
lappets in iron-red and the petals
variegated.

These follow late 17th- early 18th-
century silver forms, from which
the mask – almost like an American
Indian – is also copied. Such ewers
were usually accompanied by oval,
ribbed or shell-shaped basins, and
were as likely to be used for

washing as for drinking. They would almost certainly have been part of the private cargo.

LITERATURE
Beurdeley, *Porcelain of the East India Companies*, Cat. 49a & b, where Imari examples of ewer and basin from the service for the Duke of Chandos (c.1720) are illustrated. Scheurleer, *Chinese Export Porcelain*, fig. 104 where a similar jug but with domed foot and Portuguese arms is illustrated.

## 246
## Jug and Dish

Yongzheng, c.1728
Height of jug: 9 in (23 cm);
width of dish: 12½ in (31.7 cm)

The jug of pear shape, with plain handle and cover shaped to overlap a small sparrow beak, and with a contemporary silver hinge and shell thumbpiece. Decorated in underglaze blue with elaborate floral decoration beneath a honeycomb diaper, and a large *famille rose* armorial between palm fronds.

The dish with the same arms, but with rich *famille rose* flowers within a *rouge-de-fer* and gold stylized rim, and finely painted rose diaper in the well.

From two services made at the same time with the arms of Skinner, for one of three brothers – Richard, a London merchant, who died in 1746; Matthew, Chief Justice of Chester; or Samuel, captain of an East Indiaman, killed by the pirate Angrea in 1731 off the coast of India.

The Tower family also had two such services of identical pattern and all these must have been ordered at the same time, probably by Richard Skinner, and by Christopher or Thomas Tower, who were Joint Auditors of the Revenue.

LITERATURE
Howard, *Chinese Armorial Porcelain*, p. 171 where this jug (then in the Bullivant Collection) is illustrated; and p. 229, a similar dish.

## 247
## Jug and Dish

Qianlong, c.1738
Height of jug: 8¾ in (22.3 cm);
width of dish: 11¼ in (28.6 cm)

The jug of pear shape; the handle
with a solid scroll at the lower end,
the cover shaped to overlap a small
beak. Decorated in *famille rose*
enamels with a large armorial
between two sprays of gilt flowers.
The circular dish with the same
arms but three flower sprays in
underglaze blue.

From two services made, perhaps in
the same year, for Adriaan
Valckenier (1695–1751), who
served in Batavia from 1715 to
1741, where he was later Governor-
General, returning home after the
massacre of the Chinese in 1740. A
plate of a more elaborate service
with the same arms is illustrated
(no. 61).

LITERATURE
Ayers, Impey & Mallet, *Porcelain for
Palaces*, p. 98 where a Japanese jug
of earlier date with these arms is
illustrated.

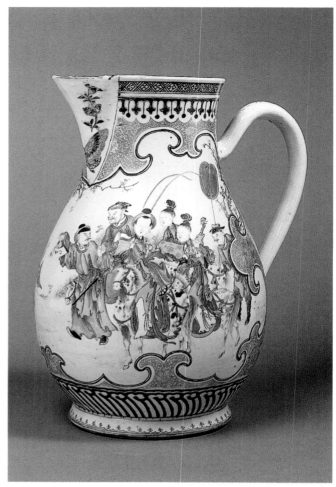

## 248
## Ewer

Qianlong, c.1750
Height: 13¾ in (34.8 cm)

Of pear shape, with heavy handle of rectangular section and 'tragic' mask beneath the spout. The decoration in bright *famille rose* enamels with peonies and branches of fruit, and a bird over rockwork.

A ewer of this form was probably not part of a dinner service, although it may have been sold with similarly decorated mugs of bell shape and used for cider or beer.

The mask under the spout originated as a silver form in the 17th century, and was copied in Chinese porcelain as early as about 1710 (see the pair of *famille verte* ewers no. 245). This almost theatrical mask of exaggerated form, however, is in imitation of continental porcelain of the 1740s.

EXHIBITED
Metropolitan Museum of Art, International CINOA Exhibition, October 1964–January 1975, illustrated in Cat. p. 82, pl. 76.

## 249
## Jug

Qianlong, c.1750
Height: $12\frac{1}{2}$ in (31.8 cm)

A large jug or pitcher, of standard baluster shape, decorated on the body with a mounted Chinese ceremonial procession with men, women and musicians within an irregular gilt scrolling border between underglaze blue formal decoration.

This unusual design was probably part of a single dinner service and was almost certainly carried as Private Trade. Such a scene was not ordered from Europe, and the elaborate decoration is unusual.

## 250
## Cider Jug

Jiaqing, c.1810
Height: $9\frac{1}{2}$ in (24.3 cm)

Of barrel form with protruding spout and cross-strapped handles with spreading fern-like gilt ends. Painted with a broad band of flowers on a gold ground beneath the rim, and with two oval panels among flower sprays on the body – one with an acrobat doing handstands on a chair, while the other appears to depict a domestic dispute.

The colouring illustrates the increasing use of various shades of turquoise enamels between 1810 and 1820, while the scenes are bold and original without the appearance of copying, which was a feature of later ware.

Probably made for the American market, which was by this time the principal buyer of porcelain.

## 251
## Basin and Ewer

Daoguang, c.1840
Basin width: 12½ in (31.7 cm);
ewer height: 10 in (25.5 cm)

The basin of simple shape with turned-over rim; the ewer of barrel shape with straight jutting lip, the cross-strap handle placed very low on the body, and the cover with a seated dog of Fo. Decorated all over with a version of 'tobacco leaf' pattern incorporating very bright patches of turquoise blue and bold pink flowers.

The purpose of such bowls and ewers was for washstands, and examples still displayed on tripod wooden stands, with the basin at the top and the jug standing on a shelf below, are in bedrooms at Charlcote Park in Oxfordshire and Cherry Hill at Albany, New York – both of a somewhat later date.

The mean proportions of the jug handle, and the heavy revival of the 'tobacco leaf' pattern, both indicate a date closer to the middle of the 19th century than to its early part, when such washstands came into fashion.

LITERATURE
*Treasures of the National Trust*, 1976, chapter 8, where a tripod washstand is illustrated with jug and bowl.

## 252
# Wall Cistern

Kangxi, c.1720
Height: 13½ in (34.2 cm)

Of semi-circular fluted baluster form, with splayed foot and flat back; on the lower part a moulded mask and spout, the fluted cover with double knop finial. The decoration of Chinese Imari floral pattern, with a large armorial with supporters on the body.

The arms are of Brydges and Willoughby, for James Brydges, then Baron Brydges, who married Cassandra Willoughby as his second wife, and was created Duke of Chandos in 1719. Shortly after this, a very large dinner service was made with the Duke's arms, together with at least four (and probably eight) wall cisterns and basins – of fluted upright oval form on three pointed feet. The Duke was known as 'Princely Chandos' and lived in great splendour at his estate of Canons, at Edgware near London.

Many such wall cisterns were fitted in Europe with small brass taps, but this does not appear to have happened in this case. They were used either for holding drinking water or for water for washing hands, and were accompanied by oval basins – usually fluted.

LITERATURE
Tudor Craig, *Armorial Porcelain of the 18th Century*, p. 36 where a cistern, two basins and a jug are illustrated.
Howard, *Chinese Armorial Porcelain*, p. 181.

# Utensils

Examples, c.1640–c.1780

In their search for ever greater markets for Chinese porcelain, the Companies, as well as individual supercargoes and merchants, found uses for porcelain that were novel and sometimes short-lived.

Although candlesticks were one of the earliest European forms chosen for copying (with the exception of the dinner service), these creations did not survive the 18th century in any quantity because they were too delicate for everyday use, in spite of their decorative appeal.

Some of the finest porcelain snuffboxes and étui were mounted in silver or gold in Europe, copying models devised at Meissen.

The more utilitarian shaving bowls, cuspidors and chamber pots rivalled and closely copied silver or other metal shapes, but ceased to be made when social changes rendered them obsolete. The range of examples here is by no means comprehensive, but they give an idea of the versatility both of their potters and of European requirements.

## 253
## Candlestick

Chongzhen, c.1640
Height: 10 in (25.4 cm)

With high domed foot, above
which are a broad drip pan and tall
hollow stem. Decorated in
underglaze blue with sprays of
chrysanthemum and peony with
smaller floral sprays.

As with a number of other objects
of European design that were not
normally used in China, the
porcelain candlestick developed
exactly as its metal counterparts in
Europe. This early 17th-century
shape is known in pewter, and a
pewter stick must have been used as
a sample.

This is the earliest form of
candlestick recorded in Chinese
porcelain – the decoration matching
very closely that on pieces of the
1643 Hatcher cargo (see mustard
pots such as no. 132).

254
Candlestick

Kangxi, c.1690
Height: 8¾ in (22.4 cm)

On a domed foot, the stem with
four heavy knops and the candle
holder of tulip shape. The
decoration in underglaze blue with
leaves and flowers simply painted
on twined stems, and a band of
scrollwork at the foot.

This stick is after a late 17th-century
European brass example, the form
reflecting the somewhat clumsy
shape of the original.

## 255
## Pair of Candlesticks

Kangxi, c.1720
Height: 5⅜ in (13.7 cm)

On slightly domed, shaped hexagonal bases with shallow knops, collars and balusters beneath hexagonal nozzles; decorated on a red-speckled ground in *famille verte* enamels with floral motifs in panels.

These small candlesticks are after Queen Anne silver originals and are most likely to have been ordered privately.

Candlesticks were comparatively rare in the later 18th century, although they were sometimes made as part of elaborate armorial services.

LITERATURE
Howard, *Chinese Armorial Porcelain*, pp. 201, 502 where armorial examples for the Duncombe family of c.1720 and the Raper family of c.1750 are illustrated.

## 256
## Pair of Chambersticks

Qianlong, c.1780
Width: 5⅞ in (15 cm)

Of traditional European form with lobed saucer and upright simulated bamboo candle holder, beside it a smaller tubular holder for spills or tapers, and having an arched Chinese dragon handle; the saucer with vines and small tree rats finely modelled and applied. The painting bright, with Chinese figures and houses on a shore line.

This chamberstick was a direct copy in Chinese taste of the European chamberstick. The modelling of the tree rats and vine is particularly well done, and this type of decoration was used on garnitures and bottles.

LITERATURE
Howard, *Chinese Armorial Porcelain*, p. 641 where a plainer armorial example is illustrated.

## 257
## Two Boxes

Chongzhen, c.1640
Diameter: 1⅞ in and 1⅜ in (4.8 cm and 3.6 cm)

Decorated in underglaze blue, the smaller cylindrical box with a man sitting fishing on a river bank, the sides splashed with curving 'tails'; the larger box disc-shaped, with formal scrollwork about a central panel. The glaze of both slightly dull.

The cargo of the Chinese trading vessel sunk about 1643 contained more than a thousand small circular porcelain boxes with a great many designs. Some of the slightly larger ones had pierced porcelain liners, while those in green earthenware were designed to contain bronze mirrors (a number were found which fitted the boxes exactly).

These were used for ointments and medicinal pills, or cosmetics and patches, almost as 'compacts' are used today.

Some of the designs from this cargo of c.1643 were almost identical to those on a much smaller number of circular boxes salvaged from the Vung Tau wreck of c.1695; and in the Sale of Private Trade at East India House in March and April 1703 there were '1050 Patch boxes' sold at 2¼d each.

LITERATURE
Christie's Amsterdam, catalogue, 12–13 June 1984, p. 52 where six boxes are illustrated and Lots 600–27 list 160 boxes varying in size from 3.5 cm to 11.5 cm.
Sheaf & Kilburn, *The Hatcher Porcelain Cargoes*, p. 61 where a number are illustrated, including one with a liner.

## 258
## Circular Box

Chongzhen, c.1640
Diameter: 5½ in (14 cm)

Of *blanc-de-Chine* porcelain, with vertically ribbed sides on both cover and base, the cover moulded with raised branches of flowers and leaves. The surface dull.

A considerable number of these boxes, varying from 14 cm to 9 cm in diameter, were found when Captain Hatcher returned to the wreck of the Chinese junk of c.1643. In the cargo of the wreck found off the Vung Tau Peninsula c.1695 more than five hundred circular boxes of exactly this type, of four sizes ranging from 13 cm to 5.5 cm, were discovered. There would appear to be no difference of any sort between these wares of the two cargoes, although they were made about 50 years apart.

Their exact purpose is unclear, but in their pristine glazed condition they were attractive evidence of the delicacy of eastern porcelain, and merchants probably had little difficulty in selling them in Europe for patches, pills and other uses. However, few were known before these cargoes were salvaged.

LITERATURE
Christie's Amsterdam, catalogue, 7–8 April 1992, p. 61 where a variety of boxes from the Vung Tau cargo are illustrated.

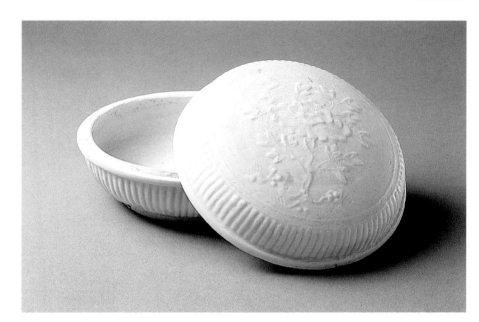

## 259
## Snuff Box
Qianlong, c.1740
Width: 3 in (7.6 cm)

Of oval bombé shape, the porcelain intricately painted on the lid in *famille rose* with two ladies and a child in a pavilion within grey scrollwork, and on the sides with alternate panels of birds and flowers and smaller puce riverscapes; the bottom similarly decorated. Inside the cover, European figures in a Meissen-style cartouche. The ormolu mounts made in Europe.

The organization that enabled these fine boxes to be made in two continents – the gilt metal frame and hinges being added in Europe – shows the sophisticated planning behind such fine Private Trade. A considerable range of scenes from erotic to armorial were mounted to make very fine boxes in imitation of the Meissen boxes which had been popular from about 1730 onwards.

LITERATURE
Morley-Fletcher, *Meissen Porcelain in Colour*, p. 95 where three similar Meissen boxes of c.1730 and c.1738 are illustrated.

## 260
## Snuff Box

Qianlong, c.1745
Width: 3 in (7.6 cm)

Of oval bombé shape, the porcelain finely painted on the outside with European figures in river landscapes within four shaped cartouches divided by gilt scrollwork, and on the inside with two Chinese pheasants. The mounts of ormolu (the gilding a little rubbed) with hinge.

Because of the fashion for Meissen boxes, this and very similar shapes were the most sought after, but round boxes of the same quality were also made.

LITERATURE
Howard, *Chinese Armorial Porcelain*, p. 316 where a round armorial snuff box is illustrated.

## 261
## Snuff Box

Qianlong, c.1760
Width: 2¾ in (7 cm)

Of rectangular form with bombé sides, the porcelain finely moulded with a basket-weave pattern and painted in flowers of Chinese and European origin. Mounts of silver.

The shape and moulded pattern must have presented a considerable challenge to the potter (a similar basket weave was employed on plates later in the 1760s). It is clear that the Chinese were copying Meissen porcelain (or perhaps Battersea enamel), and these would have been brought by supercargoes to Chinese workshops in Canton. However, the porcelain would have been fired at Jingdezhen, even if the flowers were painted in Canton.

## 262
## Étui

Qianlong, c.1750
Height: 4½ in (11.6 cm)

Of tall oval section, the fluted body and domed cover mounted in delicate ormolu chased and pierced with floral swags, with a hinged loop as a finial and press-stud catch. The painting very fine: the body with two panels each of three figures on a terrace within gilt scrollwork, the cover with small scenic panels *en camaieu*, and the fluting accentuated with gilt scrollwork in the grooves.

Étuis, used to hold needles, bodkins or toothpicks, were made in gold and in continental porcelain, and this Chinese example is a very rare object privately ordered – perhaps on behalf of a European china merchant wishing to find a competitive product, or as a private purchase by a supercargo.

## 263
## Inkwell Set
Qianlong, c.1760
Width: 6¾ in (17.2 cm)

Of three compartments with separate hexagonal 'wells', the sides of pierced honeycomb diaper, and standing on three short feet. The compartments decorated with turquoise and green diaper with gold reticulated work, and the wells with various pierced floral and scrolling decoration.

The wells were for ink (a single hole), for spare quills (seven holes) and (with fine piercing) for pounce (a powder shaken over wet ink to dry it).

A variety of types of inkwell sets are known, some including porcelain pen trays and others with small candleholders, and it is certain that orders were part of Private Trade, with the variation indicating models from different supercargoes.

LITERATURE
Howard & Ayers, *China for the West*, p. 574, a later model with pen tray and candleholder illustrated.

## 264
## Dairy Bowl

Qianlong, c.1750
Width: 8¼ in (21 cm)

A shallow circular bowl with
delicate handle and pinched spout,
decorated in underglaze blue with
river landscapes below a trellis band.

Until the discovery of the cargo of
the *Geldermalsen*, when 479 of the
548 such bowls on the shipping
invoice were salvaged, this form
was almost unknown. Even now
the exact use of such bowls –
whether for skimming in a dairy or
use in cooking or eating – is not
certain, and it is clear that the
impractical, lightly potted handle
would not long have survived with
a full bowl.

They were imported into Holland
in any quantity only for eight years
(1745–52), and probably there was
no Private Trade in this form.

LITERATURE
Jörg, *The Geldermalsen*, pp. 72–3.
Howard, *Chinese Armorial Porcelain*,
p. 772 where other pieces of a more
elaborate armorial dairy set are
illustrated.

## 265
## Pair of Bowls

Qianlong, c.1780
Width: 8½ in (21.5 cm)

On round pedestal feet rising to a
squared form at the lip, with two
pouring points and two small
looped handles. Painted on the
inside of the lip with a serrated gilt
design and floral swags and tassels,
and on the outside with a large
flower spray on either side and a
floral band round the foot.

These unusual bowls are clearly
designed for pouring, and they are
said to have had a history of being
used for tea tasting in China in the
19th century – although this may
not have been their original use.
With more practical handles, they
bear some similarity to the bowls
shown opposite (no. 264).

## 266
## Barber's Bowl

Japanese, c.1710
Width: 10¾ in (27.4 cm)

Circular, with a small semi-circular piece cut from the rim and two holes pierced and decorated on the opposite side. The rim painted in underglaze blue with Imari and *famille verte* panels, and in the centre the armorials of the city of Mechlin (Malines – in the Province of Antwerp) between two tall sprays of flowers in *famille verte*. The reverse with three sprays of flowers.

The earliest mention of barbers' bowls ordered from China is in 1669, but for much of the next century a small but steady supply found its way to Europe (there was one in the private cargo of the *Geldermalsen*, which sank in 1752). In the last decade of the 17th and first two of the 18th century, they were frequently made in Japan.

The Dutch armorials are one of a series of up to twenty-four painted in similar palettes in the early 18th century (see nos 16, 17 and 24).

LITERATURE
Howard & Ayers, *China for the West*, p. 134.

## 267
## Barber's Bowl

Kangxi, c.1715
Width: 10½ in (26.8 cm)

Circular, with a small semi-circular piece cut from the rim, decorated at the border with underglaze blue trellis overpainted with four red flowers and interrupted by four cartouches of Imari flower sprays; the centre with a large spray of flowers in a rectangular jardinière in Imari palette.

Very similar to the Japanese bowl above, but most Chinese bowls had the two holes, used for tying the bowl round the neck, in the footrim, opposite to the cut-out segment. This one has two holes in the rim, almost certainly drilled after the bowl was fired, and in imitation of the Japanese.

## 268
## Barber's Bowl

Kangxi, c.1720
Width: 13¾ in (34.8 cm)

Of oval shape with piece cut from the rim, the heavily potted porcelain with a plain moulded rim, decorated in underglaze blue with dragons and phoenix between bands of diaper enclosing an armorial. The footrim with two holes made at the time of firing.

This barber's bowl was made and decorated at the same time as a dinner service with the same arms – which are of Gosselin, and almost certainly for William Gosselin, a director of the East India Company from 1714 to 1741.

LITERATURE
Howard, *Chinese Armorial Porcelain*, p. 215.

## 269
## Cuspidor

Qianlong, c.1750
Width: 5 in (12.7 cm)

Circular, of bulbous form with wide flaring lip. The underglaze blue leaves are all that is left of an Imari design, for the red and gold have been washed away by the action of the sea.

From the cargo of the *Geldermalsen*, lost in the South China Seas in 1752, which carried this pattern without a handle, and also a slightly larger version with a handle. The V.O.C. ordered cuspidors from 1737 onwards, and the invoice for this cargo shows 299 of which 245 were salvaged. The form had remained essentially the same from about 1700.

LITERATURE
Jörg, *The Geldermalsen*, pp. 78–9.

## 270
## Pair of Vomit Pots

Qianlong, c.1750
Width: 5 in (13 cm)

In the form of a small *pot-de-chambre*, decorated with flowering branches in underglaze blue.

The *pot-de-chambre* in Chinese porcelain (a number of which were armorial and usually with lids) is recorded from about 1710 until the 19th century, but the vogue for vomit pots was fortunately short-lived, for the habit of over-eating and then vomiting was in fashion for perhaps as little as five years.

Their first recorded order from China was in 1745, and by 1750 the Dutch directors had forbidden their import, but the cargo manifest of the *Geldermalsen* mentions 606 in blue and white, Chinese Imari and enamelled ware, of which 495 were salvaged by Captain Michael Hatcher. They were invoiced as being 'in the manner of a water pot' – perhaps to mislead the directors.

This cargo must have contained the great majority of those that still exist, and their importation may have been a private venture on the part of a supercargo to clear the stock of a Chinese merchant who had these unsold from the previous year. A small number of *pots-de-chambre* were also in the cargo.

LITERATURE
Jörg, *The Geldermalsen*, pp. 80–1.

## 271
## Bourdaloue

Qianlong, c.1745
Width: 10½ in (26.7 cm)

Of elongated pinched oval shape with handle at one end; painted in orange-red, gold and *famille rose* enamels with on one side a fish, and on the other an eagle under petal coronets. The cover is missing.

The bourdaloue was named after Louis Bourdaloue (1632–1704), a celebrated preacher and called 'one of the greatest orators that France has produced' in the *Encyclopedia Britannica*. But the length of sermons by Bourdaloue and others to audiences locked in their pews meant that society ladies carried these vessels to church with them.

The relevance of the fish and eagle is discussed where a plate of this service is illustrated (no. 76).

LITERATURE
Howard, *Chinese Armorial Porcelain*, p. 423 where an armorial bourdaloue with cover for an English family is illustrated.

# Jars, Vases and Garnitures

Examples, c.1590–c.1805

Jars, vases and garnitures were intended for decoration, and their form and size developed to match the architecture and decorative features of European houses.

For centuries, the faience jar had been used in southern Europe, and in the 16th and early 17th centuries the ledges above corner fireplaces were used to display a range of the new vases that came from China. By the end of that century wall brackets and brackets round mirrors held a profusion of smaller porcelain vases.

In the early 18th century, the mantleshelf was built above Georgian fireplaces and became the home of the *garniture-de-cheminée* – an assembly of three or five (or sometimes more ) vases of two complementary shapes.

With the exception of those in armorial services, and some others which were specially designed (particularly for the Dutch market), it was the china merchants in Europe who bought vases of various sizes in bulk and sold them singly, in pairs or as garnitures, for use on a wider range of furniture including pedestals above cabinets, tables and side furniture, as well as for alcoves or hallways.

Together with animal and bird figures, the vogue was to collect miniature vases of many shapes and display them on shelves or in cabinets. A few examples of these are also illustrated below.

## 272
## Jar

Wanli, c.1590
Height: 16 in (40.7 cm)

Of massive ovoid form with six flattened sides and short neck (and cover missing), decorated in underglaze blue with six large panels, at the top of each an unusual building consisting of vertical towers below which are peacocks, elephants, dogs, and other birds and animals; prominently on two sides a double-headed eagle over a heart pierced with arrows, all beneath a coronet. The shoulders with similar panels, and the base and neck with formal decoration.

This jar bears the symbols of the Order of St Augustine, and it is recorded that a number were at the Convent of the Order founded at Macao in 1589. Other similar jars have been found in Mexico, but it is not certain whether they were made for a convent there. At this time there was a busy Spanish trans-Pacific trade from China to Mexico by way of the Philippines. In Mexico, porcelain and other cargoes were transported by land to the Gulf port of Vera Cruz, founded by Cortés in 1520, and thence onwards to Spain.

LITERATURE
Museo Nationale do Arte Antique, Lisbon, In. no. 6917 for a similar jar. De Castro, *Chinese Porcelain and the Heraldry of the Empire*, p. 29; and p. 28 where a similar jar of the same date with the emblem of the Society of Jesus is also illustrated.

## 273
## Jar

Chongzhen, c.1643
Height: 9¾ in (24.8 cm)

Oviform with broad shoulders and a cover (which may not be the one originally intended) very little larger than the mouth; decorated entirely in underglaze blue with sprays of flowers and fruit, the shoulders with panels of scalework. The glaze dull.

This vase was part of the very varied cargo of a Chinese vessel which sank about 1643 in the South China Seas en route to Batavia, and was salvaged by Captain Hatcher.

In this cargo were a wide variety of vases and jars, and these would have

been sold to Dutch merchants of the V.O.C. and probably to other private merchants on arrival in Batavia. In a great many cases it is clear that lids were selected and matched on arrival, and this accounts for their variation in size. During salvage it was found that some jars contained fruit and chutneys (*atcha*) and when this was the case, a cork stopper was used and covered with wax to preserve the contents.

LITERATURE
Christie's Amsterdam, catalogues, 14 March, 12–13 June 1984. Similar jars illustrated pp. 24, 64 (March) and p. 26 (June).

## 274
## Three Miniature Bottles

Chongzhen, c.1640
Height (tallest): 2¾ in (7 cm)

Of varying shape: double-gourd, straight-necked and trumpet-shaped; decorated in underglaze blue with floral and leaf designs, in part in formal bands.

The importation into Europe of large numbers of bottles of a great variety of shapes fed a latent desire to collect pieces of this 'new' material. This salvaged '1643 Cargo' (sold in Amsterdam in 1984) contained more than 3,500 miniature items including the smaller boxes. There is no record at this date of the Dutch East India Company ordering them, and they would have been bought by merchants as a high class souvenir trade. It was not long, however, before they were used in decorative schemes on brackets, around mirrors and in cabinets – the zenith of their popularity being the last decades of the 17th century and the first of the 18th century.

LITERATURE
Sheaf & Kilburn, *The Hatcher Porcelain Cargoes*, pls 86–7 and discussion p. 50.

275
Eight Small Vases
Chongzhen, c.1640
Height (tallest): 4½ in (11.5 cm)

As with the miniature bottles above, these small vases were made in a very large number of shapes, with straight, wide, narrow, trumpet, and onion necks, well decorated in formal patterns of flowers and leaves divided by formal bands. All these from the '1643 Cargo'.

This somewhat larger size of vase was particularly suited to arrangement on the shelves over 17th-century corner fireplaces, and on wall brackets. There is little doubt that the wide variety of shapes encouraged collecting, and these small vases were the forerunners of the *garnitures-de-cheminée* of the end of the 17th and the 18th centuries.

LITERATURE
Christie's Amsterdam, catalogue, 14 March 1984, four examples of this size illustrated, Lots 257–8 (amongst others).

red, green, yellow and aubergine.

These colours were to become known later as *famille verte* (a term first used in 1861 by Jacquemart & LeBlant) and although this term is usually applied to the late 17th and early 18th century, the 'five colour' or Wucai style had been popular in China throughout the Ming Dynasty.

Although examples of this style and date came to the West in the 17th century, this vase has a Chinese collector's mark and probably left China no more than a century ago.

LITERATURE
Butler, *Seventeenth Century Chinese Porcelain*, p. 134 where a dish in the same palette is illustrated.

## 277
## Pair of Vases
Kangxi, c.1690
Height: 7¾ in (19.8 cm)

Of squat jar shape, with long neck flaring at the top and with folded scroll-like handles on either side; decorated solely in underglaze blue with flower stems and with shading on the folded handles.

These vases are in imitation of Venetian glass, which was increasingly copied during the late 17th and early 18th centuries in Europe by the emerging glass factories of Holland and England. The somewhat clumsy translation from the glass original may well be after a wooden sample sent to China, probably for the Dutch market.

It was obviously a popular idea, for there are a number of very similar imitations – some rather taller or of different proportions. It seems probable that this was a private initiative and that the vases were entirely for display.

## 276
## Beaker Vase
Shunzhi/early Kangxi, c.1660
Height: 20¼ in (51.4 cm)

Of slightly flaring cylindrical shape, the top half decorated with an elephant, painted in fine red lines against an underglaze blue background, being washed by four men with a large tub of water in a terraced garden. The lower half with tree peonies, lotus and lily clusters in the same enamels, with

LITERATURE
Scheurleer, *Chinese Export Porcelain*, fig. 107, a 26 cm example painted in a more stylish manner in the Princesshof Museum, Leeuwarden.

## 278
## Jar

Kangxi, c.1695
Height: $15\frac{1}{2}$ in (39.2 cm)

Of baluster form; decorated in underglaze blue on a background of flower sprays, and with petal and lambrequin borders with four roundels of European ladies at their ease.

The figure illustrated is after a print of c.1685 by Bonnart entitled '*Euphrosine troisième Grace*', and there are others from different sets of French engravings of the same period of 'The Five Senses' and 'The Elements'. A larger jar is known with five roundels, and dishes are recorded with a single roundel in the centre. (See nos 5, 6 and 7 for porcelain after other engravings of this date.)

All the original engravings are of French origin and illustrate ladies in the height of fashion – it is not certain that the porcelain was destined for the French market, however, for French modes were very much copied at this period. Almost certainly these jars and platters were part of a Private Trade initiative.

LITERATURE
Howard & Ayers, *China for the West*, pp. 79–80 where three of the original engravings are illustrated. Butterfield & Butterfield catalogue, San Francisco, 9 December 1980, Lot 31 where a circular dish with a girl on a swing is illustrated.

## 279
## Covered Beaker

Kangxi, c.1695
Height: 7½ in (19 cm)

Of tall flaring form, the base domed beneath a collar and the cover gently domed with a finial above a knop. Decorated in rich underglaze blue with a design of feathery, twisting chrysanthemum scrolls; the glaze slightly dull.

This beaker, recovered off the Vung Tau Peninsula in 1990 and one of eighty of this shape (of two patterns) sold at Amsterdam in 1992, was almost certainly for decorative use. Four main sizes (about 4 inches, 7 inches, 10 inches and 12 inches) were in the cargo, and while the smallest could have

been used for drinking, the larger ones were for decoration on wall brackets or shelves.

Such shapes would have been selected by merchants in Batavia to fulfil orders for Holland.

LITERATURE
Christie's Amsterdam, catalogue, 7–8 April 1992, Lots 50–85 (where the other pattern of hatched wisteria and pine is illustrated).

## 280
## Garniture

Kangxi, c.1695
Height: 6½ in (16.5 cm)

Comprising five pieces, three of baluster form with covers and two of trumpet shape, each spirally moulded and decorated in underglaze blue with tall aster stems; the glaze worn.

It is clear from examination of this 1695 cargo that the most important part was vases and garnitures (over 7,000 vases of all sizes were sold in Amsterdam in 1992, and a considerable number were also sold in the East). This reflected the decorative arrangement of European houses in the late 17th and early 18th centuries – first piling the porcelain high on corner chimneys and later on mantleshelves, and arranging vases on wall brackets and about mirrors. The number in a garniture depended on the decorative effect required and could be from three to seven or more pieces.

The aster was already used as decoration on saucers and dishes, but the fact that this particular design has not previously been recorded on a vase may indicate that this was a major cargo, and as it never reached Europe, the design did not become popular in the same way as some others.

A particular feature of this, and almost all the other vases in this cargo, was the moulding (see also no. 281).

LITERATURE
Christie's Amsterdam, catalogue, 7–8 April 1992, Lot 181 et seq.

## 281
## Garniture Vase

Kangxi, c.1695
Height: 6½ in (11.6 cm)

A single vase from a garniture set, of baluster form with broad neck and high domed cover and finial. The decoration in underglaze blue with four lotus-leaf panels of boys holding lotus flowers (reversed) on a blue ground; the glaze worn from 300 years under the sea.

This is one of two shapes of baluster vase with this design from the cargo salvaged near the Vung Tau Peninsula; others have a narrow neck rising to a cup shape, while they are matched by an archaic *gu* shape (similar to a trumpet shape but with large central knop).

This design also is very rare, possibly because the cargo was lost and the pattern never gained popularity in Europe.

The lotus panels are moulded, as with most other vases in the cargo, and it is a particular feature of this date. Many of the designs were popular for up to thirty years, but it was soon realized that the considerable extra work involved in moulding as well as painting was not sufficiently appreciated, and the process had generally been discontinued by shortly after 1700.

LITERATURE
Christie's Amsterdam, catalogue, 7–8 April 1992, Lot 167 et seq.

282

Garniture

Kangxi, c.1705
Height: 10¾ in (27.5 cm)

Of three (originally of five) pieces, of ovoid and baluster form and moulded oval section, the vase with trumpet neck having two pierced masks, possibly originally for rings. Decorated in *famille verte* translucent enamels, the broader sides painted with exotic pairs of birds in a garden and the narrower with flower sprays. The finials moulded in petalled form.

The great variety of garnitures for mantleshelves indicates a wide variety of sources, and it is probable that Chinese merchants collected a wide range for selling to supercargoes in Canton. While the overall number was indicated by East India Company orders, the design and exact decoration could be chosen; and it is certain, too, that many of the more exceptional examples formed part of private orders.

## 283
## Pair of Vases
Kangxi, c.1715
Height: $18\frac{1}{2}$ in (47 cm)

Of squat baluster form with high domed covers, these large vases are decorated with elaborate gold scrollwork on a powder blue ground, each with four large and eight small reserves painted in *famille verte* enamels, with river landscapes and flowering branches, scholars' utensils and archaistic vessels.

The use of a powder blue ground was short-lived, stretching perhaps from 1715 to 1725, and almost always with *famille verte* panels, for undoubtedly this was an expensive and difficult process. Vases of this size were probably part of private cargo (see also no. 23).

## 284
## Garniture

Qianlong, c.1737
Height: 11 in (28 cm)

Of five pieces, three of simple pear shape and two of trumpet shape; decorated in underglaze blue with three seated and one standing figure beneath lappets of carefully diapered pattern, and with a similar band at base.

This design, known as 'The Four Doctors' or 'The Doctor's Visit to the Emperor', was the second provided by Cornelis Pronk between 1735 and 1739, and was produced in China in underglaze blue, *famille rose* and Chinese Imari (see no. 54 where further details are given).

Dr Jörg records orders for eighteen garnitures (presumably of five) between 1736 and 1739 and this must almost certainly be one – a rare example of such a garniture surviving in its original form.

LITERATURE
Jörg, *Pronk Porcelain*, pp. 76–9 where underglaze blue and *famille rose* plates are illustrated and a pear-shaped bottle in *famille rose*. Scheurleer, *Chinese Export Porcelain*, fig. 200 where a blue jug is illustrated.

## 285
## Urn

Qianlong, c.1738
Height: 21 in (53.3 cm)

Massively potted and of baluster form, the jar and cover are decorated over most of the surface with a European diamond diaper in turquoise, rose and lilac, while within shaped strapwork is a large irregular panel on either side, one with a seated figure in oriental or Turkish robe, wearing a civic crown and smoking a long pipe, the other with an oriental figure about to drink from a shallow bowl.

This is perhaps the most powerful of the designs associated with Cornelis Pronk. The original is not preserved, but the diaper and strapwork are of European design and similar to other pieces from his studio.

288
## Pair of Vases, Ormolu-mounted

Porcelain, Qianlong, c.1760
Ormolu 19th century

Height: 16 in (40.6 cm)

Of square section and flaring shape, broadening also at the base to a square pierced pedestal; two sides moulded and two sides plain, each plain face mounted with a later ormolu arched handle of vines and grapes, the ends terminating in rams'-head masks, and the footband standing on four tortoises.

The painting on the deeply moulded sides is of a mother with a child carrying a basket of flowers, the flat sides with figures by a lake beneath flowers and butterflies.

The ormolu mounts, which appear to be of the second quarter of the 19th century (but maybe later), have almost certainly been regilded, and it is arguable whether they enhance what is otherwise a fine and unusual pair of vases. There is no doubt that some of the celadon and other monochrome ware mounted in France, particularly in the mid-18th century, lends itself to this embellishment, but the busy panels of this decoration do not need these additions.

## 289
## Pair of Vases

Qianlong, c.1775
Height: 11½ in (29.3 cm)

Of baluster shape and rectangular section with stylized dragon handles, the body painted on each face with figures in landscapes and on terraces, within narrow irregular 'Y-diaper' borders in green. The necks similarly painted but separated by a band of honeycomb diaper.

The green diaper is an unusual and satisfying colour for this period – it is more usually in sepia and gold. These vases could also have formed part of a garniture, and undoubtedly they would have been part of the private cargo.

## 290
## Pair of Vases

Jiaqing, c.1800
Height: 8½ in (21.6 cm)

Each standing on an octagonal base, rising above a pedestal foot and bulbous body to a lobed trumpet neck and lip, with on either side a handle in the form of a European dragon, its wings moulded on the shoulders of the vase. Painted predominantly in a wine-purple colour, with diaper and feathering at the lip and pedestal and a number of flower sprays, with gilding on the octagonal base.

Although undoubtedly after a European original (possibly French or Italian) it has not been possible to find the inspiration for these vases. The modelling is well done and may be inspired by an earlier maiolica design. No other Chinese vases of this pattern appear to be recorded.

## 291
# Pair of Urns

Jiaqing, c.1805

Height: $17\frac{1}{3}$ in (44 cm)

Of neo-classical form, standing on square plinths with tall rectangular handles and fluted neck, the body moulded with swags, ovals and leaf fronds. The high domed covers pierced and with torch finial. Decorated in blue enamel and gold, largely following the moulding, and on one side of each in an oval the initials 'LCB . . . Memory of' and on the other side 'TW . . . Sincere Friends'.

The form and inscriptions suggest funerary vases given to a grieving friend. The funerary vase reached its greatest importance at the end of the 18th century, and paintings of Washington's tomb, and that of Louis XVI, are well known on Chinese porcelain.

Such classical vases, inspired by Italian, Sèvres and Marieberg originals, were copied in China in the late 18th century; many had inscriptions or initials, and it is clear that they were ordered privately.

LITERATURE

Beurdeley, *Porcelain of the East India Companies*, pp. 30, 67, 118 for three different versions – one funerary. Grandjean, *Dansk Ostinkdisk Porcelaen*, fig. 128 where a vase of similar but simpler form, with a sorrowing widow as the finial, is illustrated.

## 292
## Pair of Vases

Guangxu, c.1880
Height: 19 in (48.2 cm)

Of tall square section with waisted neck and flaring lip; finely painted in *famille verte* enamels, each face with a different scene – deer in woodlands, cranes on tall trees, dragons and carp in waves chasing flaming pearls – while round the neck is a four-clawed dragon with clouds and rockwork. On the base six-character Kangxi marks, although the vases are of the 19th century.

For more than a century the rich *famille rose* opaque colours had dominated Chinese porcelain taste in Europe. The reduction in orders after 1800 resulted from a number of causes: the ability of Europe to manufacture porcelain itself, the halting of all bulk orders from the East India Companies, and the wars of the 1830s to 1860s. A situation was created where, once more, Chinese workshops reverted to a tendency to make wares of quality rather than in quantity, and to revive successful styles of the past. They discovered that a revival of porcelain painted in *famille verte* enamels, often to a high level of excellence (although usually in more detail but with less artistry than earlier), found a ready, if much smaller, market in the West.

# Figures, Birds, Animals and Fish

Examples, c.1680–c.1880

From before the Tang Dynasty ceramic figures had been modelled in China – some depicting visitors from other countries – but the diversity of porcelain models introduced in the 18th century was far greater than ever before.

Many were not based on figures, animals and birds known to the Chinese, but were copied from European models introduced by supercargoes and in competition with those already popular in Europe, particularly those made at Meissen.

Since the European factories were anxious to increase their own sales, such variants made in China can only have been an attempt by the East India Companies and their servants to buy at advantageous prices – particularly for china shops in the West.

But the Private Trade greatly extended this brief by buying large numbers of other figures based on more domestic Chinese tastes, including Chinese deities and mythical animals, as well as parrots and other birds more familiar in the East than in Europe.

The resulting exchange of ideas and patterns created perhaps the most interesting group of Chinese Export porcelain.

This is also the most difficult group of porcelain to date with accuracy, for the originals are sometimes obscure or made over a long period, and while some pieces are after European originals of known date, others are based on Chinese tradition or symbolism; while yet more are most easily dated by the figures that later copied them in Europe.

## 294
## European Family

Kangxi, c.1710
Width: 6 in (15.2 cm)

Of white-glazed porcelain, modelled with a European man wearing a hat, seated with a woman and both holding glasses, while their son and daughter stand on either side, a dog at his feet while a monkey sits at hers, all on an irregular plinth.

Such figures, from Dehua in the Province of Fujian, upriver from the port of Foochow, had been made since trade with Europe was expanded at the beginning of the 17th century, but it was not until the early 18th century that large numbers were brought to Europe. Many found a place in the collection at Dresden of Augustus the Strong, and some forms were copied by Meissen.

This was probably the most popular *blanc-de-Chine* figure group of Europeans and is one which has a number of variations, some with one of the figures omitted, but always with the same European man (see no. 295 shown opposite); the name later given to the group as being of 'Governor Duff' (Diederick Duiver), the Dutch Governor-General of the East India Company, 1729–31, is of little foundation. An example of this model was in the Dresden Collection.

LITERATURE
Howard & Ayers, *China for the West*, p. 94.

## 293
## Pair of Boys

Kangxi, c.1680
Height: 13¼ in (33.6 cm)

Standing smiling and each holding a vase, their feet on a high plinth moulded with lotus leaves; each figure with a small boy clinging to the outside leg. Decorated in *famille verte* translucent enamels.

The *Hehe erxian* boys symbolized harmony, and with their smiling, inscrutable faces they were popular figures in the West in the late 17th and early 18th centuries, and were usually decorated in *famille verte* enamels. This model with the younger boys is unusual.

Some earlier, finer models show the boys together on one plinth, and there are a few later *famille rose* examples.

LITERATURE
Butler, *Seventeenth Century Chinese Porcelain*, p. 130 where a similar but earlier figure of about 1650 is illustrated.

## 295
## European with Musicians

Kangxi, c.1710
Height: 5½ in (14 cm)

White-glazed, and modelled with a European man wearing a tricorn hat seated cross-legged, a plant in a pot beside him, while two young musicians sit on the plinth on either side, both with similar hats, one playing a flute (here broken) and the other a mandolin.

The man is modelled in very similar fashion to the one in the family group above (no. 294). This smaller variation may well have been bought because it was cheaper.

LITERATURE
Donnelly, *Blanc-de-Chine*, pl. 119b.
Beurdeley, *Porcelain of the East India Companies*, Cat. 46, pl. 58.

## 296
## Taper Holder

Kangxi, c.1710
Height: 3⅝ in (9.3 cm)

In creamy white glazed porcelain,
modelled with a European man in
hat and coat carrying a bag at his
waist and holding an oar as he sits
astride a crowned sea lion, all on a
plinth with incised floral design.

Although the joss-stick holder was
familiar to the Chinese, it would
seem that there must have been (at
least in part) a model of some kind
for this amusing object, for the
crowned head of the lion is
European in concept, and the taper
holder was used in most European
houses as an essential element in the
process of lighting candles.

Very similar figures often disguised
whistles concealed in the design –
although the novelty value of this
outweighed the practicality.

LITERATURE
Howard & Ayers, *China for the
West*, p. 97.

## 297
## Guanyin

Kangxi, c.1720
Height: 10¼ in (26.2 cm)

White-glazed, and modelled seated on a rocky throne, holding on her knee a figure of a boy with a lotus. With ample robes and headdress over piled hair, and round her neck a necklace; to her left, a book.

This figure in *blanc-de-Chine* is of Guanyin, the Goddess of Mercy, and a favourite deity of expectant Chinese mothers.

The figure is modelled almost exactly as many others (where the boy holds nothing, and the necklace is replaced by a crucifix and rosary), which were brought to Europe as Christian figures with the Infant Jesus. Further figures were modelled with a European face, as the Madonna holding a figure of Christ.

There is little doubt that for about two centuries these figures became mixed, and all were purchased alike as religious icons by merchants.

LITERATURE
Howard & Ayers, *China for the West*, pp. 90–1 where a Guanyin with a cross very similar to this one is illustrated, and also a Madonna.

## 298
## Daoist Immortal

Qianlong, c.1750
Height: 4¼ in (10.9 cm)

Standing on a tall rectangular plinth pierced with an inverted heart, this white figure in dulled white glaze holds a gourd in his left hand, while his right rests on a crutch.

This figure of Litieguai comes from the wreck of the *Geldermalsen*, which sank in 1752. Sets of figures of the Eight Daoist Immortals were popular in Europe as ornaments – and this was particularly useful to the Chinese, who were able to sell them in both the oriental and occidental markets without alteration.

As well as in *blanc-de-Chine*, sets were decorated with blue and celadon glazes, and later in more varied *famille rose* enamels, often painted on the biscuit; these were supplied as sets of novelties into the 19th century.

LITERATURE
Jörg, *The Geldermalsen*, p. 101 where four from the same set are illustrated.
Sheaf & Kilburn, *The Hatcher Porcelain Cargoes*, p. 152 where all eight are illustrated.

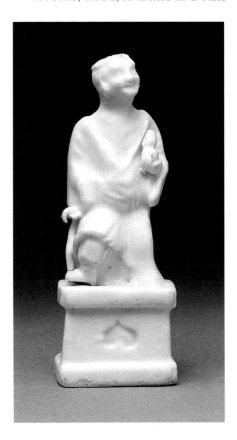

## 299
## Merchant and Dutch Lady

Qianlong, c.1740
Height of man: 16¾ in (42.5 cm)
Height of lady: 16⅝ in (42.1 cm)

The bearded man with broad black hat and yellow-lined purple coat over a patterned blue tunic with white ruff, his left arm outstretched and in his hand a red purse (his black boots on a shallow wooden plinth of later date). The lady with lace bodice and ruff and pink-lined patterned blue cloak over a rose-pink dress, with pale blue apron and yellow-lined green 'vest'.

These two figures have been assumed to be a pair in Dutch costume, and are the largest porcelain models of Europeans recorded and of comparative rarity (perhaps no more than twenty are recorded – with rather more ladies than merchants known).

Most of these merchants have suffered the loss of their extended hands, which have usually been replaced by wooden ones. This has probably obscured the meaning of the pair, for only two examples with original hands have been recorded in recent years. There is little doubt that the merchant holds a purse, and it may illustrate the age-old saga of the honest man returning with the spoils of commerce to hand them to his wife. It may also be that he is a Jewish merchant, for his hat could indicate this.

The similarity of modelling and colouring of all known examples seems to suggest a single, small private consignment.

This merchant figure has an exceptional provenance in that it is accompanied by an old label stating that it was one of two 'Dutch Merchants' formerly in the cabin of Admiral Byng, and sold with his effects in 1757 after his execution (see chapter 1). This also suggests that such figures were for purchase separately as well as in pairs.

LITERATURE
Beurdeley, *Porcelain of the East India Companies*, p. 91 (with wooden hand).
Sargent, *The Copeland Collection*, pp. 112–13 (the same pair).

## 300
## Tyrolean Dancers
Qianlong, c.1750
Height: 6 in (15.2 cm)

This headless pair (the colours washed away by the sea as part of the private cargo on board the *Geldermalsen* which sank in January 1752 and was salvaged in 1985) is here compared with a pair of Meissen dancers of the same date. Known Chinese examples in good condition are well painted in similar colours to the Meissen pair.

Undoubtedly part of the private cargo, suffering considerably when the cabin chest in which it was probably packed was swept out of the ship, while the main cargo sank slowly into the sea bed as the boat settled – see also a pheasant (no. 316) and *blanc-de-Chine* figure (no. 298) which suffered the same wear.

It is not clear whether Tyrolean dancers were available to private buyers in Canton, copied from a European sample which may have been taken in a previous season, or whether they were only ordered privately on one occasion. Certainly all those known appear to be very similar. They may also have inspired later pairs of European dancing couples.

LITERATURE
Sheaf & Kilburn, *The Hatcher Porcelain Cargoes*, p. 152, where three pairs are illustrated, one almost complete.
Sargent, *The Copeland Collection*, pp. 222, 223 for Europeans dancing, in clothes with Chinese decoration, c.1760.

## 302
# Chinese Lady and Dog

Qianlong, c.1750
Height: 8½ in (21.5 cm)

Seated on a rockwork plinth with a small spaniel-like dog in her arms, while a peacock looks at them from a rock. The enamels rich; her tunic green and hairband pale blue, the dog realistically painted in brown, and the peacock imaginatively enamelled in rose and turquoise.

The purpose of such groups – this would probably have been one of a matching pair – was both decorative and often emblematic of life in China, and by the early 1740s the European factories had also produced a variety of chinoiserie figures in similar poses. They were never produced in large numbers, but the considerable variety discussed by Sargent suggests they were available, according to taste, from china merchants in Canton.

LITERATURE
Sargent, *The Copeland Collection*, pp. 124–7 where a pair is illustrated and discussed in detail.

## 301
# Two Seated Boys

Qianlong, c.1750
Height: 4½ in (11.5 cm)

Modelled facing forward and laughing, wearing short tunics with ties about the tummy and with legs apart, one holding in his right hand a peach. Largely of plain white glaze, but the tunic glazed in grey-blue.

These charming and rare figures are all the more interesting because of their close dating as part of the cargo of the *Geldermalsen*. It is not clear whether the small number recovered (nine were sold in Amsterdam in 1986) were intended as novelties for Europe, but it would seem almost certain they were a private venture, as they were not covered by an order from the Dutch company for 'figures', and from their condition had probably been packed in a chest in a cabin and not in the hold.

It is also possible they were intended to revive the popularity of the *famille verte* boys of thirty years earlier (see no. 293).

LITERATURE
Sheaf & Kilburn, *The Hatcher Porcelain Cargoes*, pp. 156–7.

## 303
## Merchant with Dog

Qianlong, c.1750
Height: 6¾ in (16.2 cm)

Of glazed stoneware, modelled as a European in long coat and boots standing beside rockwork with a dog, raising his right hand as if in conversation. With celadon boots and flesh tinted face and hands, standing on a tan base, the coat and dog glazed in blue.

This well-observed, lifelike figure may have been modelled in Canton, where there was a considerable

industry of pottery and stoneware – the best known type being 'Shiwan' (although this differs in many respects). Although the material is different, the glazes and plinth are very similar to those of a number of the figures recovered from the cargo of the *Geldermalsen*.

Undoubtedly this man with dog, typical of the small seated dogs of the early 18th century, was bought privately.

LITERATURE
Jörg, *The Geldermalsen*, p. 100 where a group of figures with blue and celadon glazes are illustrated.

## 304
## Two European Girls

Qianlong, c.1760
Height: 5 in (12.8 cm)

Both modelled in the same pose, smiling and with right hand raised in greeting, each in long dress beneath a fur-lined gown, standing on an irregular base. Both in red dress, but one with pale green gown standing on a green base, the other with blue gown standing on a white base.

The models very closely copy Meissen originals produced in the 1750s, which may have had more delicately painted flowered dresses, and which were also copied by other European factories. It seems most likely from their rarity that this was a small private venture.

LITERATURE
Howard & Ayers, *China for the West*, p. 619 where a Meissen original is also illustrated.

## 305
## European Boy

Qianlong, c.1760
Height: 5½ in (14 cm)

Modelled in fancy dress – a Turkish-style costume with military jacket and tall fez-like cap with cockade – standing on a white base. His tunic is red, his trousers blue and his short-sleeved jacket green, while his hat is black with a yellow hanging plume.

The Central European child's dress used in the Meissen original was copied in China, and as with the two girls (no. 304), he was probably produced in competition with European factories. Only a small number are known in Chinese porcelain.

LITERATURE
Howard & Ayers, *China for the West*, p. 619 for a very similar example.

## 306
## Chinese Man and Girl Drinking

Qianlong, c.1770
Width: 6 in (15.2 cm)

Both seated on a plinth by hollow rockwork; the man, with unbuttoned tunic, offering a hesitant girl a cup of wine. He in a blue tunic, red breeches and black boots, the girl in a pale blue-and-yellow patterned dress, by a scarlet-and-turquoise rock.

The implications of this model are obvious, and her doubts about accepting his offer of wine leading to something else are well expressed.

This is one of a number of similar models of Chinese men and women with extended meanings – a girl examines the leg of a seated man; a girl examines the ear of a seated man; and a girl sitting on the knee of a man with open shirt, are of the same period – which attracted private buyers in porcelain shops in Canton.

LITERATURE
Sargent, *The Copeland Collection*, pp. 130–1, a girl examining the leg of a seated man.

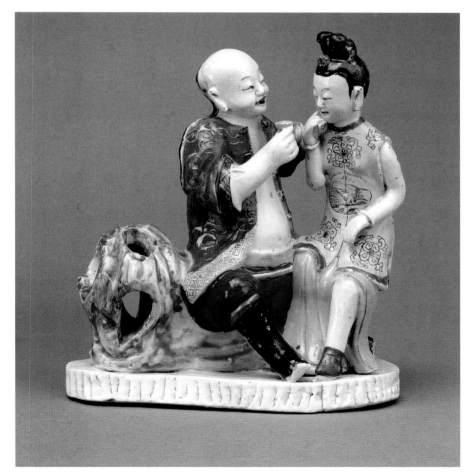

## 308
## Pair of Ladies with Candleholders

Qianlong, c.1780
Height: 11½ in (29.2 cm)

Standing on rectangular plinths of European design, these chinoiserie figures hold metallic-shaped vases as candleholders. The heads, which are separate and have appended a small leaden weight, can be turned at will and display a European 'ideal' of a Chinese face. The tunics black, decorated with gold and with purple sleeves, the long skirts patterned yellow, and the plinths with a moulded 'rope' design in black and gold, edged in red and yellow.

These figures, almost certainly copied from a European (possibly German) model, derive inspiration from the Chinese ladies at no. 307, and were probably copied unconsciously in China as largely European. The turning head, however, was not new to the Chinese repertoire.

LITERATURE
Howard & Ayers, *China for the West*, p. 614.

## 307
## Pair of Ladies with Candleholders

Qianlong, c.1775
Height: 16¾ in (42.6 cm)

Standing demurely with finely painted Chinese tunics and holding *gu*-shaped vases, the hair in a high double bun held in place with a pin. The tunics in rich blue, red and gold with yellow lining over a more delicate dress showing below, with green plinths. The vases painted in brown and pink with mountain and river scenes.

Pairs of Chinese figures with candleholders enjoyed considerable popularity in the second half of the 18th century and there are a number of variants. In this case the vase could double as a candleholder.

LITERATURE
Sargent, *The Copeland Collection*, pp. 133–5 where a more attractive version with lotus candleholders is illustrated.

## 309
## Chinese Matron

Qianlong, c.1790
Height: 20½ in (52 cm)

Majestically robed, standing holding in one hand a scroll (both hands are removable), a mantle covering her hair, and wearing a cross on a chain. Her hair is grey and her white robes, scattered with red and blue flowers and leaf sprays, are lined in red and black with gilding, a line of green at the hem.

This large figure of a Chinese matron was designed for the western market, but exhibits some contradictions: although essentially a figure of Guanyin (who traditionally holds a scroll) she is wearing a cross. The figure was probably to be used as decoration, and undoubtedly bought as part of private cargo.

LITERATURE
Beurdeley, *Porcelain of the East India Companies*, p. 204 where a pair are illustrated.
Howard & Ayers, *China for the West*, pp. 614–15 for a similar figure.

## 311
## Pair of Boys

Probably Guangxu, c.1880
Height: 8½ in (21.7 cm)

Well modelled as if climbing stairs, but with flat backs and slot for hanging on a wall, each holding a vase. Both equally well decorated in *famille rose* with flowers on the white glaze, but one coat with *famille verte* trimming in translucent enamels, and the vases in the style of the early 18th century.

It is the mixture of palettes, which would have been unlikely to occur in the 18th century, which suggests these are well painted 19th century figures. The use of porcelain figures as wall decoration unsupported by brackets was also much more common in the late 19th century. The quality, however, is excellent, and this applies to much work of the period.

## 310
## Preacher

Probably Guangxu, c.1880
Height: 10½ in (26.7 cm)

Standing with right hand holding his coat and left holding a hat, his long hair pale brown, his tunic and shirt with intricate green-and-red floral design on a pale 'golden' background and his knee breeches black and floral above leggings and black shoes; at his side a cross and rosary.

This very rare figure is reputed to be of a Portuguese missionary, but in spite of the rosary (something a Chinese modeller might assume was worn by all Christian preachers), his clothes and his face, hair and hat could be mistaken for those of John Wesley (the centenary of whose death fell in 1891). It is relevant that the last quarter of the 19th century saw a short period of high quality *famille verte* enamelling (see no. 292).

LITERATURE
Howard & Ayers, *China for the West*, p. 651, a rare figure of 'Our Lady of Lourdes', c.1850.

312
Cricket Cage

Kangxi, c.1700
Height: 4 in (10.2 cm)

Very finely and crisply modelled with a phoenix before rockwork with lotus flowers, one claw on the head of a turtle, whose eye acts as a hinge for a small pierced brass door enclosing a cricket cage. Decorated in *famille verte* translucent enamels splashed on the biscuit.

This is an unusual model and of superior quality, probably made for the Chinese market at a time when small porcelain animals and birds, principally dogs and parrots, were imported in very large quantities by the East India Companies during the last decade of the 17th and first two of the 18th century.

Such objects could certainly, however, have been bought as special curiosities by a merchant as private trade.

LITERATURE
Sargent, *The Copeland Collection*, pp. 87–9 where two cockerels and four miniature parrots of this date are illustrated.

### 313
## Pair of Hawks

Qianlong, c.1740
Height: 6¾ in (17.1 cm)

Modelled in mirror image with heads turned, perched on rocky mounds with one claw raised and the other fully extended (the rockwork and body hollow).

Painted in bright *famille rose* enamels of crimson, red, orange, yellow, turquoise blue and violet, the feathers modelled individually and picked out in brown, black and gold, the rockwork speckled.

It is difficult to gauge the exact date of such birds – nor is this of the greatest importance – for these models were bought over a period of about three decades from c.1735 to 1760 or later. It is the quality and variety of the enamelling which matter, and this pair, although probably the smallest size made, are very finely painted. Such birds undoubtedly cost more and were bought in numbers by private traders for clients in Europe.

LITERATURE
Sargent, *The Copeland Collection*, pp. 146–9 which illustrates the largest size (almost 21 inches).

### 314
## Pair of Pheasants

Qianlong, c.1740
Height: 10¾ in (27.4 cm)

Gracefully modelled in mirror image with heads turned and feathers individually moulded, perched on two tiers of rockwork. The colours range from crimson through the entire spectrum and are picked out in gold and black – the necks and head being particularly bright; the rockwork is speckled and splashed.

These birds have most of the decorative characteristics of the pair of small hawks (no. 313), the feathers and rockwork being particularly similar. They represent the finest and most natural models of pheasants made, and would have been at the top of the price range available to the private merchant.

This model was copied with a high degree of accuracy in the 19th century by Samson.

## 315
## Cockerel

Qianlong, c.1745
Height: 12⅝ in (32 cm)

Standing on rockwork with one leg up and the body turning towards the viewer, the feathers very lightly modelled. The painting in a full spectral range of colours, the comb and wattles enamelled in mottled red, the eye yellow like the beak, with pupils in black.

This model of a cockerel had probably been available since the 1730s, sometimes in plain white glaze only. This version, which was made facing either way, was enamelled in China (see also no. 318) in an attractive and semi-realistic colouring with multi-coloured chest feathers. The opportunity to decorate in a variety of ways was freely taken, and two other versions are in the Copeland Collection. The Chinese symbolism, of a bird of good fortune, embodied in these figures would have been largely lost on European private merchants, who would have bought them for their decorative value.

LITERATURE
Sargent, *The Copeland Collection*, pp. 141–5 where two pairs of this date but different colouring are illustrated.

## 316
## Pheasant

Qianlong, c.1750
Height: 10¼ in (26.2 cm)

Modelled with head turned sharply over the back, with meaner chest and head larger in proportion. The feathers not modelled individually, and the stand giving the appearance of a wooden stump rather than rockwork. The glaze worn away.

It is most instructive to see this model of a pheasant of almost certain date, which was part of the private cargo of the *Geldermalsen*, which sank in January 1752.

Much of the porcelain cargo had enamels quite well preserved, but this was tightly packed in boxes and protected to a large degree from rubbing by the sand. Evidently this pheasant, and the only other complete bird recovered, were in a merchant's chest in a cabin which probably broke open and exposed its contents to the wear of the sea.

LITERATURE
Sheaf & Kilburn, *The Hatcher Porcelain Cargoes*, p. 158 where this pheasant is illustrated.
Private collection, from the same cargo: a parrot with some enamels remaining, on high domed rockwork.

## 317
## Hawk

Qianlong, c.1750
Height: $10\frac{5}{8}$ in (27.2 cm)

In the same pose as the smaller pair of hawks shown on page 262 (no. 313) but on rather more stylized, streaked rockwork, and the feathers less well modelled. Enamelled in realistic tones of brown, the feathers well painted, and contrast added by a chestnut breast and splash of turquoise at the top of the beak; the rockwork in tones of blue, celadon and brown.

This is a well-proportioned bird but not quite of the same quality, nor quite as early as the pair above. Nevertheless, such birds were undoubtedly an exciting part of the Private Trade, and chosen for appeal and price by merchants.

LITERATURE
Sargent, *The Copeland Collection*, pp. 150–1 where two somewhat larger brown hawks have stronger colouring.

## 318
## Pair of Cockerels

Qianlong, c.1760
Height: $13\frac{1}{3}$ in (33.6 cm)

Modelled in a very similar manner to the cockerel on page 263 (no. 315), but originally only the pupil of the eye and the rockwork enamelled in blue in China. The dull red combs, wattles and legs, and the beaks, eyeballs and claws all cold painted (or very lightly fired).

As cost started to play a greater part in the ever widening popularity of Chinese birds, it was understandable that less expensive methods of decoration were employed.

LITERATURE
Howard & Ayers, *China for the West*, p. 584 where a rather earlier example with worn cold painting is illustrated.

## 319
## Pair of Doves

Qianlong, c.1775
Length: 7¼ in (18.4 cm)

Well modelled with heads facing forward and standing on shallow rockwork, carefully painted with grey-shaded pink beaks and red eyes with black pupils, the rockwork lightly coloured.

These are a slightly superior model to those with white glaze only, and the colouring of the rockwork is perhaps as good an indication as any of the date (which is not yet certain).

It was, perhaps, the increased production of models of various birds at the Meissen factory in the 1740s and '50s that encouraged private merchants to order similar (and other) birds from China in competition with the European models.

LITERATURE
Howard & Ayers, *China for the West*, pp. 586–7 where a pair of white-glazed birds with turned heads is illustrated.

## 320
## Pheasant

Qianlong, c.1780
Height: 14 in (35.6 cm)

Modelled more stiffly than the earlier pheasants with head slightly turned over a very straight body, the feathers not modelled separately, the rockwork more regular. The painting more simplified and repetitive than on earlier birds, but with a wide range of colours.

This pheasant has lost some of the charm of its predecessors, but is brightly coloured. It would, however, undoubtedly have been part of the private trade.

LITERATURE
Howard & Ayers, *China for the West*, pp. 588–9 where a similar pair, of slightly earlier date, are illustrated.

## 321
## Pair of Owls

Qianlong, c.1790
Height: 10¼ in and 10½ in (26.2 cm and 26.8 cm)

Realistically modelled, and of somewhat benign appearance, with feathers moulded and splayed at the tail, the bases pierced. Painted naturally in rather pale brown with black, yellow and pale green eyes, the claws shaded and the rockwork in black and turquoise. The base flat and with a pierced hole.

The indefinite details suggest copying from a drawing rather than a model, although English porcelain owls were being made by the 1780s.

Very few examples are known, although a pair (one with black claws) was in the Mottahedeh Collection.

LITERATURE
Howard & Ayers, *China for the West*, pp. 592–3.
Tait, 'Birds in European Ceramic Art' *Apollo*, April 1958, fig. XVII.

## 322
## Pair of Parrots

Jiaqing, c.1810 or later
Height: 8 in (20.3 cm)

Well modelled in an alert, aggressive pose with some moulding of the feathers, the colours bright and tropical. With the glazes applied in washes, including unusual shades of wine colour and grass-green picked out in black, the eye rings in dull orange set in black and the green heads with yellow beaks, the rockwork in turquoise-green and oily black.

These naturalistic poses and unfamiliar colouring indicate the 19th century, Jiaqing c.1810 or later, while the type of moulding for the feathers contrasts unfavourably with the finely painted birds of the mid-18th century.

This is a rare model of which only one other pair is recently recorded.

LITERATURE
Christie's London, catalogue, 1 November 1993, Lot 27, where a pair with slightly different colouring is illustrated.

## 323
## Parrot

Japanese, c.1860
Height: 8½ in (21.8 cm)

In smoothly potted white-glazed porcelain with slight modelling of the wings to suggest feathers, the head turned, standing on a tall piece of rockwork. The eye only coloured in rich dark blue.

The re-entry of the Japanese into the European and American porcelain trade in the later 19th century brought to the market a new range of animals and birds based on models of an earlier date, but with different glazes and poses. This bird has been called a hawk, but it seems more likely to be intended as a parrot.

## 324
## Pair of Cockerels

Probably Guangxu, c.1880
Height: 8 in (20.3 cm)

Modelled as was usual for cockerels with head slightly to one side, and sitting heavily on rockwork. The painting bright and well executed, but with less variation than on 18th-century models, and with a fungus-like flower growing on the rockwork. It is of interest that a fungus is also painted on a large pair of cranes (no. 326), and such additions can be a sign of later copying. The colours have a bold, almost brash quality which is common to other examples of this later 19th-century period, when a number of 18th-century models were revived and decorated to a high standard of quality, but without their softer grace.

## 325
## Pair of Pheasants

Probably Samson of Paris, c.1880
Height: 22¼ in (56.6 cm)

These very large birds are modelled in similar proportions to the late 18th-century Chinese example, no. 320 above, but with no modelling of the feathers, while the rockwork is more realistic. The painting, however, is very different – the colours being either over-bright with some shades out of the spectral range, or faded (as on the neck), with contrasting shading and bright, metallic gilding.

These European birds in the Chinese style, which are exceptionally large (a mid to late 19th-century tendency which saw very large Chinese dogs and *blanc-de-Chine* figures, cranes etc and did not confine itself to Chinese porcelain), show all the hallmarks of conscious copying of earlier models without achieving the easy balance of colours and form that was such a factor in their popularity.

By this date a wide range of European and Chinese figures could be bought in New York department stores, either ordered directly or by their agents in China. There is little doubt that size by then was equated with importance.

## 326
## Pair of Cranes

Probably Guangxu, c.1880
Height: 15½ in (39.4 cm)

Well modelled in an alert pose with
heads thrown back and very straight
legs, the feathers lightly moulded;
the pierced tree stump with fungus
and a branch of pine growing on it.
The colours contrasting with
feathers outlined, the stump and
pine brightly coloured in yellow,
red and green.

Such very large models were typical
of the second half of the 19th
century. The dating is not precise,
but the considerable stimulation
provided after the opening up of
trade with Japan about 1870, and
the end of the wars of the previous
two decades, makes the late date
probable.

The crane had been a favoured bird
in porcelain since the 1750s, when
models which were either simpler
(and frequently white), or shorter-
bodied with tall necks and brighter
colouring, were produced.

LITERATURE
Sargent, *The Copeland Collection*,
pp. 164–5 for an earlier type c.1750.

## 327
## Hound

Kangxi, c.1720
Length: 4½ in (11.4 cm)

Modelled as an excited barking hound with tail over its back, enamelled in black with white paws, on a flat plinth in translucent green.

This local breed in unusual pose is unlike most of the models of small dogs imported in quantities in the early 18th century by the East India Companies. Those were enamelled on the biscuit, usually with green glaze, and seated. It is likely, however, that this would have been a private commission.

LITERATURE
Howard & Ayers, *China for the West*, p. 583 where reference is made to a similar pair in the National Trust Collection at 'Ascott', Buckinghamshire.

## 328
## Two Seated Hounds

Yongzheng, c.1730
Height: 6 in (15.4 cm)

Seated with expectant faces, the tongues well formed, and one with head turned over its shoulder, with an off-white glaze. Probably not intended as a pair, for the collar ornaments vary, as does the glaze on the eyes and the teeth.

With cargoes often containing many hundreds of hounds of this breed, it was inevitable that china shops bought and sold large numbers, which were not intended by their makers to be 'pairs'. This does not mean that they were not sold suitably matched in china shops in Europe.

The simple modelling of these hounds makes it likely that they were part of Company cargo.

LITERATURE
Sargent, *The Copeland Collection*, pp. 100–101 where two smaller hounds in this attitude and colouring are illustrated.

## 329
## Pair of Seated Hounds
Qianlong, c.1750

Height: 9¾ in (24.8 cm)

Modelled in similar fashion to the two preceding examples, but with perhaps less expression in the faces. The colouring red-brown with white chests and inside of the legs, the faces splashed with brown, and the collars green, with tassel and bell.

Without comparison of a large number of these hounds it is difficult to be certain of their date, but the simplicity of the modelling of the paws, and somewhat exaggerated features, tend to guide the dating to 1750 or later.

It was at this time that a much wider range of dogs, after European models, was introduced (see nos 330–333).

### 330
### Pair of Pug Dogs

Qianlong, c.1750
Height: 10 in (25.4 cm)

Seated on their haunches and
looking straight ahead with mouth
closed but tongue protruding, the
tail crimped but bushy. Painted
with pale salmon-coloured chest
and face, the back, legs, jowls and
head with finely drawn black hair,
the ears clipped showing pink and
the eyes pale blue and black, with
red collar and gold bell.

If only because of the clipped ears –
a European habit in the 18th
century – these dogs are clearly
based on Meissen originals of the
early 1740s produced by Joachim
Kaendler. They are stiffer than
earlier breeds of local hounds, and

this seated version is unusually large
and considerably rarer. They were
almost certainly bought as part of
the Private Trade.

LITERATURE
Sargent, *The Copeland Collection*,
pp. 189–91, two tan pugs.
Howard & Ayers, *China for the
West*, pp. 598–9, a slightly smaller
black version with white chest.

### 331
### Pair of Pug Dogs

Qianlong, c.1760
Height: 7 in (17.8 cm)

Modelled as a matching pair, each
with head slightly turned, these pug
dogs have long ears, very heavy
(possibly exaggerated) jowls and a
bushy tail, plainer than that of

no. 330. They are painted in deep tan with black pupils on white eyes, with red collar and gold bell.

These smaller, more winning models of pugs are also more natural (without European clipped ears) – but the eyes have become simplified to black pupils on white.

This type of pug dog was not as popular as the spaniels below (no. 332), but they were undoubtedly part of the Private Trade.

## 332
## Pair of Seated Dogs

Qianlong, c.1770
Height: 7 in (17.8 cm)

Modelled as a matching pair seated on their haunches, each with head turned, and with expectant faces and bushy tails. Painted in grey with fine brush strokes and tawny patches at the nose, with red collars about their necks, each with a gilt ball.

These spaniels are known in pale red, brown and black, both seated and lying down. The earlier ones probably had the mouth open and tongue showing, but the mouth was later closed so that the additional work in inserting the tongue was not necessary. Much of their charm emanates from the decoration itself, for the modelling (largely in two sizes) is standard.

LITERATURE
Sargent, *The Copeland Collection*, pp. 184–5 (dark brown and of this model) and pp. 186–7 (iron red and brown, both seated and lying down).

### 333
### Pair of Seated Hounds

Qianlong, c.1770
Height: 11¾ in (30 cm)

Modelled with large pig-like faces, ears alert, the mouth slightly open with protruding fangs in an aggressive stare, the tails bushy and curling. The bodies intricately painted with black fur with white patches.

These large and unusual hounds have been called Tibetan mastiffs, and their looks appear to relate them to an oriental breed rather than a European one, although their pose is more in keeping with the models after Kaendler (no. 330).

They would undoubtedly have been part of a private cargo.

### 334
### Cow

Qianlong, c.1770
Length: 7½ in (19.2 cm)

Modelled standing on a rectangular plinth with cut corners, with tail flicking her flank and standing four square with head slightly turned. The markings splashed in black, similar to a Friesian but more exactly painted with orange-red flowers, the hooves and horns gilded.

This model of a cow, which is based on a Dutch Delft original – perhaps inspired by an earlier Meissen example – is known with various markings, some quite fanciful (such as the flowers on this example), and with black and gold hooves.

Sargent notes that in 1746 the Dutch East India Company sent a tin-glazed model to China for copying, with an order for 120 pairs of an earlier model. He also records that the cows painted with flowers at the neck are based on festivities held in Delft, when 'cows were decorated with flowers and had their hooves and horns gilded for a procession.'

LITERATURE
Sargent, *The Copeland Collection*, pp. 228–9, note 5, Leiting Fourest, who mentions the flower-decorated cows and records such a pair in the Rijksmuseum, Amsterdam.

### 335
### Goat

Qianlong, c.1790
Length: 6 in (15.2 cm)

Plumply modelled with head turned and beard folded back, on a rounded rectangular base; painted with pale aubergine horns and splashed grey markings, red eyes with black pupils and loops of streaked yellow/brown on a green base.

This is an unusual figure and the head is not well proportioned. It could well have been sold to complement the cow, but there is no record of a European original in this case.

## 336
## Deer

Jiaqing, c.1810
Height: $11\frac{1}{4}$ in (28.7 cm)

Modelled with head turned and a spray in its mouth, standing somewhat awkwardly with one foot raised on a rock and the body supported by rockwork modelled with a sacred fungus. The painting realistic, with finely drawn light brown hide and with spots reserved in the painting, the rockwork black with brown fungus and turquoise leaves, all on a carefully-made rectangular base.

It is natural that deer should be shown accompanied by the sacred fungus, for it is credited with being the only animal that can find it. Models of deer are comparatively rare, and those that are brown vary greatly. The technical problem of firing a creature with four legs is overcome by the support and plinth, nevertheless this model is deliberately more stylized than many.

LITERATURE
Sargent, *The Copeland Collection*, pp. 158–9, 216–17 and 246–7 illustrate three more naturalistic deer but with similar markings.

## 337
## Dog

Probably Jiaqing, c.1810
Height: 5 in (12.8 cm)

Simply modelled seated on its haunches, its flat head staring to the front, with floppy ears and long straight tail, with a collar and bell; all in white porcelain except for the eyes, which have black pupils painted on the biscuit.

This gentle dog, perhaps a puppy, was made at the end of a period in

which many tens of thousands of dogs of different breeds were supplied in similar poses. His breed is uncertain, and lack of colouring meant that it would not have been expensive. Chinese porcelain dogs were unusual in the 19th century after this date.

LITERATURE
Howard & Ayers, *China for the West*, p. 600.

## 338
## Three Horses

Perhaps Guangxu, c.1880
Height of largest: 11 in (28.6 cm)

All modelled standing in a simple pose, two of the same size and one slightly larger, with a very white glaze, the mane smoothly and neatly formed and the legs slender. The eyes with black pupils on biscuit ground.

Although these horses may be compared with a sheep of the same type of modelling and glaze, and with eyes of the same type, in the Mottahedeh Collection, the stance of the horses is in a later, more realistic, style and quite unlike other horse models recorded. A horse of this form, but enamelled as a 'strawberry roan', is also recorded. In the absence of other comparative models, the date of c.1880 is speculative.

LITERATURE
Howard & Ayers, *China for the West*, p. 601 where two horses of earlier date are illustrated. Compare also the sheep of this type, p. 605, then thought to be early 19th-century.

## 339
## Pair of Carp

Japanese, c.1690

Height: 8¾ in (22.3 cm)

Modelled leaping upwards with curved tails, in the bend of which sits a clothed boy, all on a moulded wave base. The painting in pale purple-pink, mouths red, and waves and spray in splashes and swirls of green; the boy dressed in a white spotted tunic and wearing a red head-band.

This is arguably the most attractive version of Japanese late 17th-/early 18th-century carp, and would have been imported from Japan, through Batavia, by the Dutch company.

LITERATURE

Ayers, Impey & Mallet, *Porcelain for Palaces*, p. 189, where two other versions of these carp but without boys are illustrated.

## 340
## Pair of Carp

Jiaqing, c.1800
Height: 11¼ in (28.6 cm)

Modelled apparently as vases, standing on their splayed tails and with mouths wide open, decorated in orange-red with gilt-shaded scaling, and black pupil on white eyes.

Such fish may have been utilitarian, but they were also amusing, and were probably an attempt at continuing the popularity of carp as tureens in the preceding half-century. Jörg mentions a fish wall-vase salvaged from the 1779 wreck of the Dutch East Indiaman *Woestdvijn*, although this may have been an earlier model of a single vase formed of two carp.

LITERATURE
Sargent, *The Copeland Collection*, pp. 212–15, one tureen in this colour with exactly this type of scaling, dated 1750–70.
Ayers, Impey & Mallet, *Porcelain for Palaces*, p. 286 – an English double carp vase in white, dated 1760–5.

# The Mother of the West

With the introduction of so many European influences and models into the Chinese repertoire, it was almost inevitable that the quality of Chinese design would become lost among the conflicting pressures of occidental design and cost-consciousness.

That this did not entirely distort the Chinese genius for porcelain is evident in these three final examples, made over nearly two centuries, using appropriately the legend of Hsi Wang Mu – 'Mother of the West'.

As Howard Hansford writes: 'Hsi Wang Mu, Queen Mother of the West, Royal Lady of the West. A fabulous being reputed to dwell in a palace on the K'un-lun Mountains, where she presides over the hosts of the genii and guards the peaches of immortality.'

## 341
## Deep Dish

Kangxi, c.1710
Width: 11 in (28 cm)

With shaped, lobed rim and deep well, this dish is decorated in *rouge-de-fer*, gold and *famille verte* enamels; with a maiden-goddess bearing a spray of fruit on a terrace, while a spotted yellow deer runs beside her, looking up. The rim in *rouge-de-fer* and gold, the design in imitation of Kraakware.

This is Hsi Wang Mu, 'Mother of the West', painted freely and in an animated pose, in a manner certain to please the European private market.

## 342
## Plate

Qianlong, c.1760
Width: 9 in (23 cm)

Decorated in underglaze blue, with a finely painted honeycomb-diaper border interrupted six times on the rim with stylized characters; within a leaf-shaped outline painted with floral scrollwork a figure of a goddess bearing a basket of flowers, while a deer looks up faithfully.

This Qianlong plate of the goddess Hsi Wang Mu is typical of the finely painted but stiffer underglaze blue work being done between 1755 and 1770 (sometimes on soft paste, or very white glazed porcelain). It also typifies the endless attraction and mystique of the Orient for the West.

## 343
## Two Figures of Hsi Wang Mu

Probably Guangxu, c.1880
Height: 24 in (60.8 cm)

Massively but very finely modelled, these two almost identical figures are of ladies with hair piled high and adorned with flowers, the folds of their robes deeply modelled, with one hand raised, while standing beside each on a rockwork plinth are deer looking up, with baskets of flowers on their backs.

These figures of the 'Mother of the West' are notable for their size (as were other pieces of this date, see no. 325 and no. 326) and are slip cast, having a smooth finish to the inside modelling. Although as yet unfashionable and late in the story of *blanc-de-Chine*, they might well be seen in the future as masterpieces of craftsmanship.

As with so much else in Chinese porcelain bought by traders from the West, the mythical figure of Hsi Wang Mu with her deer recalls a time when Chinese porcelain for export to Europe was as yet undreamed of.

# Bibliography

Archer, Michael, *Irish Delftware*, exhib. cat. (Castletown House, County Kildare, 1971).

Ayers, John, *The Baur Collection. Chinese Ceramics*, 4 vols (Geneva, 1968–74): vol. 2 *Ming Porcelains and Other Wares* (1969); vol. 3 *Monochrome-glazed Porcelains of the Ch'ing Dynasty* (1972); vol. 4 *Painted and Polychrome Porcelains of the Ch'ing Dynasty* (1974).

Ayers, John, *Oriental Ceramics. The World's Great Collections, 6: Victoria & Albert Museum* (Tokyo, 1975).

Ayers, John; Impey, Oliver & Mallet, J.V.G., *Porcelain for Palaces – The Fashion for Japan in Europe 1650–1750* (London, 1990).

Beurdeley, Michel, *Porcelain of the East India Companies*, translated by Diana Imber (London, 1962).

Beurdeley, Michel (in collaboration with Schipper, Kristofer, Chang Fu-Jui & Pimpaneau, Jacques), *Chinese Erotic Art* (Vermont/Tokyo, 1969).

Beurdeley, Michel & Raindre, Guy, *Qing Porcelain: Famille Verte, Famille Rose* (London, 1987).

Bondy, Walter, *Kang-Hsi, Eine Blüte-Epoche der chinesischen Porzellankunst* (Munich, 1923).

Boxer, C. R., *Fidalgos in the Far East, 1550–1770. Fact and fancy in the history of Macao* (The Hague, 1948).

Boxer, C. R., *The Dutch Seaborne Empire 1600–1800* (London, 1965).

Boyer, Marthe, *Things Chinese from the 17th and 18th Centuries in the National Museum of Denmark* (*Studia Serica Bernhard Karlgren dedicata*, Copenhagen, 1959).

Brancante *see* Da Fonseca Brancante.

Brawer, Catherine Coleman, *Chinese Export Porcelain, from the Ethel (Mrs Julius) Liebman and Arthur L. Liebman Porcelain Collection* (Elvehjem Museum of Art, University of Wisconsin–Madison, 1992).

Bushell, S., *Oriental Ceramic Art*, illustrated by examples from the collection of W. T. Walters, text edition (New York, 1899).

Butler, Joseph T., 'Chinese Porcelain Figures of Westerners', *Antiques* (February 1961).

Butler, Sir Michael; Medley, Margaret & Little, Stephen, *Seventeenth Century Chinese Porcelain from the Butler Family Collection* (Virginia, 1990).

Campos e Souza, José de, *A propósito do livro Porcelaine de la Companie des Índes de Michel Beurdeley* (privately printed Oporto, 1962).

Castro e Solla, Count, *Ceramica brasonada*, 2 vols (Lisbon, 1928–30).

Chaffers, W., *Marks and Monograms on Pottery and Porcelain* (London, 1863; 6th edn. London, 1876).

Chang, Tien-tse, *Sino-Portuguese Trade from 1514 to 1644* (Leiden, 1934).

Charleston, R. J. & Ayers, John, *Meissen and Oriental Porcelain: The James A. de Rothschild Collection at Waddesdon Manor* (The National Trust, London, 1971).

Chêng Tê-k'un, 'Some Chinese Islamic "magic square" porcelain', *Journal of Asian Art*, no. 1 (Lee Kong Chian Museum, Nanyang University, Singapore, 1964).

Copeland, Pamela C., 'Oriental Porcelain Frivolities', *Antiques* (May 1966), pp. 709–17.

Crisp, F. A., *Armorial China* (privately printed London, 1907).

Crossman, Carl L., *A Design Catalog of Chinese Export Porcelain for the American Market* (Peabody Museum, Salem, 1964).

Crossman, Carl L., 'The Rose Medallion and Mandarin Patterns in China Trade Porcelain', *Antiques* (October 1967), pp. 553ff.

Crossman, Carl L., *The China Trade Export Paintings, Furniture, Silver and other Objects* (Princeton, NJ, 1972).

Da Fonseca Brancante, Eldino, *O Brasil e a louça da India* (São Paolo, 1950).

Daggett, Charles & Shaffer, Christopher, *Diving for the Griffin* (London, 1990).

Dapper, Dr Olfert, *Gedenkwaerdig bedryf der Nederlandsche Oost-Indische Maetschappye op de kunste en in pet Keizerrijk Varr Taising of Sina* (Amsterdam, 1670).

de Castro, Nuno, *Chinese Porcelain and the Heraldry of the Empire* (Oporto, 1988).

De Hullu, J., 'De Porseleinhandel der Oost-Indische Compagnie en Cornelis Pronck als haar Teekenaar', *Oud Holland* (1915), pp. 52ff.

D'Entrecolles, Père, *Letters from Ching-te-chen, 1712 and 1722*, repr. as appendix in Stephen W. Bushell, *Description of Chinese Pottery and Porcelain, being a translation of the T'ao Shuo* (Oxford, 1910).

Donnelly, P. J., *Blanc-de-Chine* (London, 1969).

Dublin, Municipal Gallery of Modern Art, *Chinese Ceramics*, exhib. cat. (Dublin, September 1967).

du Boulay, Anthony, *Christie's Pictorial History of Chinese Ceramics* (Oxford, 1984).

Ducret, Siegfried, *Meissner Porzellan bemalt in Augsburg, 1718 bis um 1750*, parts 1 and 2 (Brunswick, 1972).

Dumas, Jacques, *Fortune de Mer à L'Ile Maurice* (Paris, 1981).

Du Sartel, O. *Porcelaine de Chine* (Paris, 1881).

Edinburgh, Royal Scottish Museum, *Chinese Pottery and Porcelain* (Edinburgh, 1955).

Farnham, K. & Efford, K., *Catalogue of the Reeves Collection* (Washington and Lee University, Virginia).

Feller, John Q., *The Canton Famille Rose Porcelains* (Salem, 1982).

Fitzgerald, C. P., *China: A Short Cultural History* (revised ed. London, 1950).

Forbes, H. A. Crosby, *Yang-ts'ai: The Foreign Colors, Rose Porcelains of the Ch'ing Dynasty*, exhibition catalogue (China Trade Museum, Milton, Mass., 12 February–27 June 1982).

Ford, Barbara Brennan & Impey, Oliver R., *Japanese Art from the Gerry Collection in The Metropolitan Museum of Art* (New York, 1989).

Funchal, Museum da Quinta das Cruzes, *Catalogo da Exposicao da Porcelana da Companhia das Indias* (1960).

Garner, Sir Harry, *Oriental Blue and White* (London, 1954).

Garner, Sir Harry, 'The Origins of Famille Rose', *Transactions of the Oriental Ceramic Society 1967–69* (London, 1969), pp. 1–16.

Gill, Conrad, *Merchants and Mariners of the 18th Century* (London, 1961).

Godden, Geoffrey A., *Oriental Export Market Porcelain and its influence on European Wares* (London, 1979).

Gordon, Elinor, *Collecting Chinese Export Porcelain* (New York, 1977).

Gordon, Elinor (ed.), 'Chinese Export Porcelain', *Antiques Magazine Library*, New York, 1977.

Grandjean, Bredo L., *Dansk Ostindisk Porselaen, importen fra Kanton c. 1700–1820* (Copenhagen, 1965).

Hackenbroch, Yvonne, 'Chinese Porcelain in European Silver Mounts', *The Connoisseur* (June 1955), pp. 22–8.

The Hague, Gemeentemuseum, *Chinese ceramiek* by Beatrice Jansen (The Hague, 1976).

Harrisson, Barbara, *Swatow* (Leeuwarden, 1979).

Hatcher, Michael & Thorncroft, Antony, *The Nanking Cargo* (London, 1987).

Hervouët, François & Nicole with Bruneau, Yves, *La Porcelaine des Compagnies des Indes à Décor Occidental* (Paris, 1986).

Hildburgh, W. L., 'Chinese Painted Enamels with European Subjects', *Burlington Magazine*, LXXIX (1941), pp. 78–89.

Hobson, R. L., *Chinese Pottery & Porcelain*, 2 vols (London, 1915).

Hobson, R. L., *The Later Ceramic Wares of China* (London, 1925).

Hobson, R. L., *Catalogue of Chinese Porcelain & Wedgwood Pottery . . . in the Lady Lever Art Gallery, Port Sunlight* (London, 1928).

Hobson, R. L., Rackham, B. & King, W., *Chinese Ceramics in Private Collections* (London, 1931).

Holmes, J. B. Sanders, 'Fitzhugh and Fitz Hughs in the China Trade', *Antiques* (January, 1966).

Honey, W. B., *Guide to the Later Chinese Porcelain* (Victoria & Albert Museum, London, 1927).

Honey, W. B., 'Dutch Decorators of Chinese Porcelain', *Antiques* (February 1932), pp. 75–80.

Honey, W. B., *The Ceramic Art of China and the other Countries of the Far East* (London, 1945).

Honor, Hugh, *Chinoiserie. The Vision of Cathay* (London, 1961).

Howard, David Sanctuary, 'Chinese Porcelain of the Jacobites', *Country Life* (25 January 1973), pp. 243ff., (1 February 1973), pp. 289ff.

Howard, David Sanctuary, *Chinese Armorial Porcelain* (London, 1974).

Howard, David Sanctuary, 'Porcelain from China and Japan', *Treasures of the National Trust*, chapter 8 (London, 1976).

Howard, David Sanctuary, *New York and the China Trade* (New York Historical Society, New York, 1984).

Howard, David and Ayers, John, *China for the West* (London, 1978).

Hudson, G. F., *Europe and China. A Survey of their Relations from the earliest times to 1800* (London, 1931).

Huitfeldt, Johanne, *Ostindisk porselen i Norge* (Oslo, 1993).

Hunter, William, *The Fan Kwae in Canton before the Treaty Days, 1825–1844* (London, 1882).

Hyde, J. A. Lloyd, 'Yesterday and Today of Oriental Lowestoft', *Antiques* (June 1931), pp. 447–8.

Hyde, J. A. Lloyd, *Oriental Lowestoft, with Special Reference to the Trade with China and the Porcelain Decorated for the American Market* (New York, 1936; 2nd edn., Newport, 1954).

Hyde, J. A. Lloyd, *Oriental Lowestoft, Chinese Export Porcelain, Porcelaine de la Cie des Indes* (Newport, Monmouthshire, 1964).

Hyde, J. A. Lloyd & Espirito Santo Silva, Ricardo, R., *Chinese Porcelain for the European Market* (Lisbon, 1956).

Hyvonen, Heikki, *Chinese Porcelain in Finland* (Forssa, 1986).

Jacquemart, A. & Le Blant, E., *Histoire de la Porcelaine* (Paris, 1862).

Japan Society, *The Burghley Porcelains*, exhib. cat. (New York, 1986).

Jenyns, Soame, *Later Chinese Porcelain: The Ch'ing Dynasty, 1644–1912* (London, 1951).

Jenyns, Soame, 'The Chinese Porcelain in the Topkapi Sarayi, Istanbul', *Transactions of the Oriental Ceramic Society*, 1964–6.

Jenyns, Soame, *Japanese Porcelain* (London, 1965).

Jörg, C. J. A. *Pronk Porcelain, Porcelain after designs by Cornelis Pronk*, exhib. cat. (Groninger Museum, 25 April– 8 June 1980 and Haags Gemeentemuseum, 20 June– 24 August 1980).

Jörg, C. J. A., *Porcelain and the Dutch China Trade* (The Hague, 1982).

Jörg, C. J. A., *Interaction in Ceramics, Oriental Porcelain and Delftware*, exhib. cat. (Hong Kong Museum of Art, 6 January–15 February 1984).

Jörg, C. J. A., *The Geldermalsen, History and Porcelain* (Groningen, 1986).

Jörg, C. J. A., *Chinese Export Porcelain – Chine de Commande from the Royal Museums of Art and History in Brussels*, exhib. cat. (Hong Kong, 1989).

Jourdain, Margaret and Jenyns, R. Soame, *Chinese Export Art in the Eighteenth Century* (London and New York, 1950).

Keil, Luis, 'Porcelanas Chinesas do seculo XVI com inscricoes em Portugues', *Boletim da Academia Nacional de Belas-Artes*, x (Lisbon, 1942).

Keyes, Homer Eaton, 'Lowestoft, what is it?', *Antiques* (parts I–VI, March, May, November 1928; March, June, August 1929).

Keyes, Homer Eaton, 'The Cincinnati and their Porcelain', *Antiques*, XVII, 2 (February 1930), pp. 132–6.

Keyes, Homer Eaton, 'American Eagle Lowestoft', *Antiques* (June 1930), pp. 530–3.

Keyes, Homer Eaton, 'American Ship Lowestoft', *Antiques* (June 1931).

Keyes, Homer Eaton, 'Liberty in the Chinese Trade', *Antiques* (November 1931), pp. 298–9.

Keyes, Homer Eaton, 'Lowestoft Exclusively American', *Antiques* (April 1932), pp. 171–5.

Keyes, Homer Eaton, 'Quality in Oriental Lowestoft', *Antiques* (December 1937), pp. 290–4.

Kisch, B., 'Europerien auf China-Porzellan', *Artibus Asiae*, VI, 3/4 (1937), pp. 272–82.

Kjellborg, Sven, T., *Svenska Ostindiska Compagnierna 1731–1813* (Malmö, 1974).

Krahl, Regina (ed. Ayers, John), *Chinese Ceramics in the Topkapi Saray Museum, Istanbul* (London, 1986).

Lang, Gordon, *The Wrestling Boys – An Exhibition of Chinese and Japanese Ceramics from the 16th to the 18th Century in the Collection at Burghley House* (privately printed 1983).

Le Corbeiller, Clare, 'Design sources of early China Trade Porcelain', *Antiques* (January 1972), pp. 161–8.

Le Corbeiller, Clare, 'Crosscurrents in China Trade Porcelain', *Antiques* (January 1974), pp. 145–50.

Le Corbeiller, Clare, *China Trade Porcelain, A Study in Double Reflections*, exhib. cat. (China House Gallery/China Institute in America, New York, 25 October 1973–27 January 1974).

Le Corbeiller, Clare, *China Trade Porcelain: Patterns of Exchange* (Metropolitan Museum of Art, New York, 1974).

Lee, Georgina E., *British Silver Monteith Bowls including American and European Examples* (Byfleet, 1978).

Lee, Jean Gordon, 'Philadelphians and the China Trade 1784–1844' (1984).

Leite, Jose Roberto Teixeira, *As Companhias das Indias e a Porcelana Chinesa de Encomenda* (São Paulo, 1986).

Little, Mrs Frances, 'America's East Indiamen and the China Trade', *Antiques* (January 1929), pp. 27–31.

Lloyd Hyde *see* Hyde.

London University, Percival David Foundation of Chinese Art, *Illustrated Catalogue. Section 2: Ch'ing Enamelled Wares*, by Lady David (London, 1958).

London, Victoria & Albert Museum, *Handbook to the Gulland Bequest of Chinese Porcelain* (London, 1949).

Lunsingh Scheurleer, D. F., 'De Nieuwe Stadsherberg in het lj voor Amsterdam op Chinees porselein', *Antiek* (May 1968), pp. 484ff.

Lunsingh Scheurleer, D. F., 'Dutch and Chinese Mustard Pots', *Antiek* (1972–3), p. 192.

Lunsingh Scheurleer, D. F., 'Opnieuw een decor met twee papegaaien en een versierung van bloemenmanden', *Antiek* (October 1973), pp. 234–41.

Lunsingh Scheurleer, D. F., *Chinese Export Porcelain. Chine de Commande* (London, 1974; New York, 1974).

Lunsingh Scheurleer, D. F., 'Chinees bordjes met Don Quijote en Sancho Panza', *Antiek* (March 1975), pp. 804–8.

Lunsingh Scheurleer, D. F., 'The Dutch at the Tea-table', *The Connoisseur* (October 1976), pp. 85–94.

Macintosh, Duncan, *Chinese Blue and White Porcelain* (2nd ed., London, 1986).

Miedema, H., *Swatow* (Leeuwarden, 1968).

Miller, B. D. H., 'Oxford in Chinese Export Ware', *Oriental Art* (Summer 1966), XII, pp. 99ff.

Morley-Fletcher, Hugo, *Meissen* (London, 1971).

Morse, H. B., *The Chronicles of the East India Company trading to China: 1635–1834*, 5 vols (Cambridge, Mass., 1926–29).

Mottahedeh, Suzanne S., 'Numismatic Sources of Chinese Export Porcelain Decoration', *The Conniosseur* (October 1969), pp. 111–18.

Mudge, Jean McClure, *Chinese Export Porcelain for the American Trade 1785–1835* (Newark, Delaware, 1962).

Mudge, Jean McClure, *Chinese Export Porcelain in North America* (New York, 1986).

Nelson, Christina H., *Directly from China – Export Goods for the American Market, 1784–1930* (Peabody Museum, Salem, 1984).

New York, China Institute in America, *Animals and Birds in Chinese Art*, exhib. cat. (1967–68).

New York, China Institute in America, *China's Influence on American Culture in the 18th and 19th Centuries*, exhib. cat. by Henry Trubner and William Jay Rathbun (New York, 1976).

Norman-Wilcox, Gregor, 'Jesuit China: A Misnomer in China Trade Porcelains', *Los Angeles County Museum of Art Bulletin*, XVI, 4 (1964), p. 19.

Oriental Ceramic Society, *The Animal in Chinese Art*, exhib. cat. with introduction by P. J. Donnelly (London, 1968).

Palmer, Arlene, M., *A Winterthur Guide to Chinese Export Porcelain* (New York, 1976).

Philips, John G., *China-Trade Porcelain. An Account of its Historical Background, Manufacture, and Decoration and a study of the Helena Woolworth McCann Collection* (London, 1956).

Philips, John G., 'Design sources of early Chinese Trade Porcelain', *Antiques* (January 1972).

Picard, R., Kerneis, J. P. & Bruneau, Y., *Les Compagnies des Indes: Route de la Porcelaine* (Paris, 1966).

Reeves Collection *see* Farnham, K. & Efford, K.

Rinaldi, Maura, *Kraak Porcelain* (London, 1989).

Roth, Stig, *Chinese Porcelain imported by the Swedish East India Company* (Gothenburg, 1965).

Rückert, Rainer, *Meissener Porzellan 1710–1810. Ausstellung im Bayerischen Nationalmuseum. Katalog* (Munich, 1966).

Rudolph, Richard C., 'Chinese Armorial Porcelain in Mexico', *Archives of the Chinese Art Society of America*, XV (1961), pp. 13–20.

Sargent, William R., *The Copeland Collection, Chinese and Japanese Ceramic Figures* (Peabody Museum, Salem, Mass., 1991).

Scott, Rosemary E. (ed.), *The Porcelains of Jingdezhen* (Percival David Foundation, London, 1993).

Shangraw, Clarence & Von der Porten, Edward, *The Drake and Cermeno Expeditions, Chinese Porcelains at Drakes Bay, California 1579 and 1595* (San Francisco, 1981).

Sheaf, Colin & Kilburn, Richard, *The Hatcher Porcelain Cargoes, The Complete Record* (London, 1988).

Smith, Philip Chadwick Foster, *The Empress of China* (Maritime Museum, Philadelphia, 1984).

Spero, Simon, *Worcester Porcelain* (Institute of Arts, Minneapolis, 1984).

Spriggs, A. L., 'Oriental Porcelain in Western Paintings 1450–1700', *Transactions of the Oriental Ceramic Society 1964–66* (London, pp. 73–88).

Staehelin, Walter A., *The Book of Porcelain, The manufacture, transport and sale of export porcelain in China during the eighteenth century, illustrated by a contemporary series of Chinese watercolours* (London, 1965).

Taipei, National Palace Museum, *Selection of Masterworks in the Collection of the National Palace Museum* (Taipei, 1974).

Tait, Hugh, 'The Commedia dell'Arte in glass and porcelain', *Apollo* (October 1963).

Tiffany, Osmund, Jr, *The Canton Chinese, or an American's Sojourn in the Celestial Empire* (Boston, Mass., 1849).

Trubner, Henry & Rathbun, William Jay, *China's Influence on American Culture in the 18th and 19th Centuries*, exhib. cat., China Institute in America/China House Gallery, New York, 8 April–13 June 1976, and Seattle Art Museum, Seattle, 7 October–28 November 1976).

Tudor-Craig, Sir Algernon, *Armorial Porcelain of the Eighteenth Century* (London, 1925).

Tudor-Craig, James, 'Armorial Porcelain from China', *Country Life Annual* (1967).

Van Goidsenhoven, J. P., *La Céramique Chinoise sous les Ts'ing* (Brussels, 1936).

Van Goidsenhoven, J. P., *La Céramique Chinoise* (Brussels, 1954).

Van Oort, H. A., 'Het wijnkopje van Ch'ien-lung', *Antiek* (1971–2), pp. 257–60.

Van Oort, H. A., 'De verzameling Chinees porselein van het Topkapi Museum in Istanbul', *Antiek* (1972/3), pp.128–9.

Van Oort, H. A., *Chinese Porcelain of the 18th and 20th Centuries* (Lochem, Holland, 1977).

Vecht, A., *Frederick van Frytom* (Amsterdam, 1969).

Veiga, Jorge Getulio, *A Porcelana da Companhia das Índias* (Brazil, 1986).

Volker, T., *Porcelain and the Dutch East India Company, as recorded in the Dagh-Register of Batavia Castle, those of Hirado and Deshima and other contemporary papers, 1601–82* (Leiden, 1954; repr. 1971).

Volker, T., 'Vroeg Chine de Commande', *Museum Boymans van Beuningen Bulletin*, IX, 3 (Rotterdam, 1958), pp. 108ff.

Volker, T., *The Japanese Porcelain Trade of the Dutch East India Company after 1683* (Leiden, 1959).

Wästfelt, Berit, Gyllensvärd, Bo & Weibull, Jörgen, *Porcelain from the East Indiaman Götheborg* (1991).

Wathen, James, *Journal of a Voyage in 1811 and 1812 to Madras and China* (London, 1814).

Weiger, Roger Armand, *Bonnart, Personnages de Qualité 1680–1715* (Paris, c.1956).

Werner, E. T. C., *A Dictionary of Chinese Mythology* (Shanghai, 1932; 2nd ed. New York, 1961).

Williams, C. A. S., *Encyclopedia of Chinese Symbolism and Art Motives* (New York, 1960).

Williamson, G. C., *The Book of Famille Rose* (London, 1910; Rutland, Vermont/Tokyo, 1970).

Woodward, C. S., *Oriental Ceramics at the Cape 1652–1795* (Cape Town/Rotterdam, 1974).

Zimmermann, Ernst, *Chinesisches Porzellan*, 2 vols (Leipzig, 1913).

# Index

Note: Numbers in ordinary type refer to catalogue entry numbers; numbers in **bold** refer to the pages in chapters and introductory paragraphs to each section of illustrations.